THE *REAL BOOK* ABOUT

BUFFALO BILL

THE *REAL BOOK* ABOUT

Buffalo

Illustrated by Robert J. Lee

GARDEN CITY BOOKS, GARDEN CITY, NEW YORK

Bill

By ADOLPH REGLI

REAL BOOKS

EDITED BY
HELEN HOKE

BY ARRANGEMENT WITH FRANKLIN WATTS, INC.

To my sister
MABEL
who shares with me a deep feeling
for the *real* West

ACKNOWLEDGMENTS

The writings about Buffalo Bill Cody are so extensive and the accounts of his Western adventures so varied that it is often difficult to sift fact from fiction to present the true picture of this great American's life.

The blame for this rests largely upon the publicity men and press agents who advertised Buffalo Bill's stage plays and Wild West shows. They wrote many stories about Mr. Cody that were simply not true. In other cases, they took incidents in his life and enlarged upon them until the original facts were all but lost.

Buffalo Bill's autobiographies suffer from the same weakness. Prepared for him by others, these accounts of his life carried over some of the "tall tales" that were first written to lure customers to his shows. It is not surprising that in time Buffalo Bill himself was unsure of the facts.

Several individuals were liberal with their time and efforts to assist the author in gathering needed material. My sister, Esther Regli, head librarian of the

Wauwatosa (Wisconsin) Public Library, combed the stacks for usable information. Professor W. S. Campbell (Stanley Vestal) of the University of Oklahoma pointed out numerous sources and offered original material.

Norman F. Anderson of Minneapolis, Minnesota, and Scott C. Hatch of North Platte, Nebraska, were others who extended their aid generously.

To all of these, the author gives grateful thanks.

ADOLPH REGLI

CONTENTS

Chapter 1

THE RESCUE OF TURK

Billy Cody heard Turk's warning bark deep in the woods. He crouched behind a fallen tree at the edge of a little clearing and waited tensely.

Soon the dog's excited yip, yip, yip sounded closer, and Billy squeezed the grip of his rifle.

Suddenly a deer burst through the brush not more than a dozen feet from the seven-year-old hunter. The buck paused under an oak, his full rack of antlers lifted high, his nose twitching to catch the scent of danger ahead.

Open-mouthed, Billy stared at the beautiful animal. His hands shook, but he was powerless to move another muscle.

The buck delayed his flight only a moment. With graceful leaps, he bounded across the clearing and vanished into the brush on the other side.

Not until then did Billy think of his gun. He started to raise it, but too late. A few swaying twigs gave the only hint of the buck's passing.

At that moment, Turk charged into the clearing. His bark broke off into a mournful yelp when he

The buck bounded across the clearing

sighted Billy still crouched in his hiding place. The dog, a large gray hound that would never take a prize for looks, made a half-hearted spurt after the buck, then turned back and lay panting on the grass. His disgust was boundless.

Billy walked slowly from behind the fallen tree. Head down, he approached the dog. "I know, Turk, I should have had that deer. He almost stepped on me, he was that close, but I . . . I . . . It was buck fever, Turk. I don't know why it happened. Next time I won't get buck fever. You just wait . . . I promise."

Turk turned his head and refused to look at his young master.

Billy let the dog rest for several minutes. He thought of his parents and five sisters in camp beside a creek not far away. They were depending on him to bring in some game for their evening meal.

They'd be satisfied with a few rabbits or a wild turkey, he knew. But when he had had a chance to surprise them with a deer, he hadn't even raised his rifle.

Just thinking about it made the young hunter's cheeks burn. Here he was, all of seven years old, and acting as though he'd never had a gun in his hands. Turk was right. Billy felt that he had disgraced himself completely.

In the weeks since his father, Isaac, had sold his farm near Le Claire, Iowa, and started the family westward, the Codys had traveled across the prairie at an easy pace. Billy's mother, Mary, and the girls rode in the family carriage while he and his father looked after the three farm wagons, covered with canvas to protect the household goods, food, and clothing.

It was the spring of 1853 and Isaac Cody, like many of his neighbors, had caught the "western fever." Thousands of people were moving to Oregon and California.

Restless by nature, Mr. Cody could no longer

resist the urge to join the great migration. Perhaps there was still gold to be found along the Pacific coast.

The Codys planned to stop first at Weston, Missouri, where Isaac's brother, Elijah, ran a store that supplied emigrant parties. From Weston, the family would pick up the trail across the plains.

The thought of living "out West" excited young William Frederick Cody, even though his days in Iowa had been full and active. Ever since he was four years old, he had ridden horses. He rarely went anywhere except in the saddle, with Turk trailing along. Few riders twice his age equaled his skill as a horseman. And when it came to shooting a gun, Billy was a match for most men.

He could hardly wait to see the vast rolling plains everyone was talking about. What fun he would have with his dog and horse, roaming for miles and miles without a building in sight. He agreed with his father, Iowa was too crowded.

Billy took pride in the trust his parents placed in him. He was allowed to ride ahead of the wagons to pick campsites and hunt game. But now the pain of his humiliation checked his daydreaming and he called to the dog.

"Come on, Turk. Maybe we'll see another deer. We can't go back to camp with nothing."

The dog was on his feet in a bound. Hunting was

his chief interest in life, and he needed no urging to resume the chase. Sprinting ahead of Billy, he was soon lost in the thick underbrush.

Now and then Billy heard a low bark as Turk signaled his position. He listened in vain for the high-pitched yips that told him the dog was on the trail of an animal. Billy began to wonder what had happened to all the game.

He pushed his way through a tangle of brush. Twigs pulled at his long blond hair and he raised an arm to protect his face. Gradually the scrub thinned out, and he came to a river bank lined with larger trees. Turk trotted to Billy's side and rested on his haunches.

"I guess there's nothing on this side of the river," Billy said. "Maybe you'd better swim across and scare up something over there. Go on, Turk. Start swimming."

Reluctantly, the dog entered the river. His dislike for water was plain as he glanced back to see whether Billy had changed his mind.

"Go on, Turk. Hurry up."

Soon Turk was fighting the strong current, which carried him downstream a little distance. Upon reaching shore, he shook himself mightily and began to range the woods for something to chase.

Billy stood motionless beside a tree for many minutes. High above him a squirrel leaped from one bough to another. But Billy paid no heed. After seeing the large buck he wasn't interested in squirrels.

It was a long time before Turk appeared. Then he came out of the brush some distance upstream. Billy noticed that the dog was limping. Turk must have scraped a foreleg leaping over a windfall or bruised it on a rock.

"Come over here, Turk," Billy called. "Let me look at your leg."

The dog hesitated for a moment before entering the cold river again. Once in the water, he made hard work of swimming against the current, which began to drag him downstream. Billy had to move along the bank to keep abreast of the dog.

"Come on, boy . . . come on," Billy urged. "You're nearly halfway across."

Turk was in trouble, Billy realized after a moment. He was not at home in the water at any time, and with an injured leg he was barely able to make headway. He barked weakly.

As though the word had been spoken, Billy knew that Turk was calling for help. Dropping his rifle instantly, he ran a few steps, plunged into the river and began to swim.

Turk's head vanished before Billy reached him. Swimming as hard as he could, the young hunter splashed forward. He saw a gray shadow below the river's surface. Lunging for it, he dug his fingers into the thick skin of the dog's neck and started to raise the shaggy head.

Turk came up snorting and began to thresh about, almost slipping from Billy's grasp.

"Easy, boy, easy," Billy warned. "You'll drag me . . . you'll drag us down."

Together the boy and his dog drifted with the current. Swimming with one arm, Billy clung to Turk with the other.

The dog's dragging weight felt like a log to Billy. He put all his power into his strokes and kicked hard to make headway. He could gain only a few inches against the river tugging at him with its cold grip.

Straining at each stroke, Billy battled to reach shore. He noticed that he was drifting toward a bend in the river where the current swept sharply against a bank several feet high. Some brush, nearly awash in the stream, curved down until a few branches almost touched the surface. If he could only reach it!

With his last reserve of energy, Billy swam for the river bank. His outstretched fingers tore several leaves from a bush. He grabbed at another branch, missed, and then caught the last tiny limb. It dipped under Billy's weight, sagged into the water, and then held.

Pulling Turk closer, Billy eased him toward the bank and felt him gain a slippery foothold. Turk scrambled out of the river and barked a signal of triumph.

Easing himself forward, Billy took hold of another branch and rested for a minute, his legs still in the water. He was too tired to do more. On the bank Turk paced about nervously, whimpering softly.

At last Billy was able to crawl up the bank, where he sat to recover his breath. Turk stopped his whines and licked Billy's hand.

"That's all right, Turk. Now we're even."

Billy took off his shirt and wrung out the water. He did the same to his pants and then remembered Turk's injury. He examined the dog's leg and found a bruise but nothing more. Turk would be all right in a day or two.

Dressed again, Billy walked back along the river bank until he found his rifle. Carrying it in the crook of his arm, he headed back toward camp. Turk limped along at his heels.

"I'd like to know what else can go wrong," Billy muttered. "We'll have a slim supper tonight. All I can show for my hunt is wet pants and——"

Suddenly Turk yelped an alert and bounded off, his injury forgotten. Billy stopped, listening intently. Soon the dog's yip, yip, yip sounded to the left, and Billy waited, his rifle raised.

This time he felt calm, his nerves steady. When a fat doe flashed into view, running swiftly between the trees fifty yards away, he fired just once. The deer flinched, ran on a few steps and dropped to the ground.

Turk reached the doe first. His bark rang with joy and approval.

"Well, Turk, we got our deer after all," Billy said happily. "We'll have a good supper now."

Chapter 2

SEARCH FOR A NEW HOME

Billy Cody gazed ahead eagerly for a glimpse of Weston. The Cody wagons had left Iowa a week before and were now well into Missouri. That morning Billy's father had promised they would reach the home of Uncle Elijah by nightfall.

From the top of every rise of land over which the wagon trail twisted, Billy scanned the rolling hills ahead. The afternoon was well spent before he saw a cluster of houses and stores far down a long valley.

"That must be Weston, Father," he called.

"That's it," Isaac Cody agreed. "It's the biggest town in this part of the West."

An hour later, the Codys were welcomed by Uncle Elijah and his wife. Mary Cody and the five girls were glad of this chance to stop and rest. How good it would be to sleep in beds again after camping out for weeks! But Billy wanted to go on at once.

"It's May already and we shouldn't waste any time, Father," he said. "We'll never get to California if we stick around here."

Mr. Cody smiled at his son's impatience. "California won't run away. We'll get there."

Elijah cut into his brother's words. "Isaac, you're making a mistake if you expect to get rich in California. Talk to some of the gold hunters who are coming back. You'll go broke out there, just as they have."

Billy looked at his uncle with a frown. "Not go to California!" he thought. Before he could speak, his uncle went on.

"There's lots of land—good, rich land—right across the river in Kansas. It'll make you the finest farm you ever saw. And here's another idea. Take a load of goods from my store and trade with the Kickapoo Indians out beyond Fort Leavenworth. While you're there, look around and see what Kansas has to offer. It's the coming state, Isaac. You'll do far better than you will by making that killing drive two thousand miles to the west coast."

Isaac Cody thought for a minute. "Maybe you're right, Elijah."

"I know I'm right. Leave Mary and the girls here while you hunt up a homestead. I'll send a guide along who knows all that country well. Do a little trading on the side and you can earn more than your keep until your first crops are harvested."

"That sounds fine, Elijah," Isaac said. "I'll do that."

"May I go with you, Father?" Billy asked quickly, trying to hide his disappointment over Elijah's plan. "I can help trade with the Indians."

"I'll need you, all right, Billy. But it will take me a few days to get ready."

While waiting for his father to stock his trading wagon, Billy roamed about Weston, catching the excitement of the busy border town. The stores were crowded with people getting ready to start West. Horses lined the hitch rails, and the thump of boots sounded on the boardwalks of the main street.

At last Mr. Cody was ready to leave, and Elijah brought the guide he had promised. To Billy's delight, Elijah offered him a spirited horse to ride while his own pony rested. Turk, made nervous by the crowded city, refused to budge from Billy's side for fear of being left behind.

The little trading party crossed the Missouri on a ferry and took the road to Fort Leavenworth a few miles up the river. The Army post, consisting of stone buildings around a wide parade ground, swarmed with soldiers and horses. The sound of bugles, drums, and shouted orders echoed among the barracks, officers' quarters, warehouses, and stables.

It was the first fort Billy had ever seen, and he was too amazed by all the activity to say a word. He regretted that he could not stop to watch the skillful riding of the cavalrymen and the marching of the foot soldiers.

After passing the fort, Billy came upon a sight even more startling. A flat area, acre upon acre, looked like a sea packed with sailboats. But instead of boats, the objects were covered wagons, hundreds of them.

Great herds of oxen, horses, and mules, stacks of hay, long sheds, blacksmith shops, and other buildings were also in view. The crack of whips and the shouts of the teamsters rang out above the busy flat.

"Hopping hoptoads!" Billy exclaimed. "Father, what is all this?"

"It's the supply depot of Russell, Majors & Waddell, the company that hauls government freight. Their trains carry Army supplies to forts and posts all over the West. Some even go across the mountains, to Fort Bridger and Utah."

Again Billy wished there was time to see the bullwhackers yoke up their oxen and start their long journeys. But the guide hurried on as though this was a sight too common for a second look.

A wagon trail, already cut deeply into the Kansas sod, led away from the river. Billy's father said it was the beginning of the road to Salt Lake and California.

After following the trail for three miles, they came to a trading post. A crowd of rough-looking men stood around the front of the store.

"This is Rively's place, Cody," the guide said.

"Rively does a good trade with settlers already out here. It's the meeting place, too, of every tough in these parts. You can hear hot talk about the slavery question, if you care to listen."

Billy glanced at his father. He had often heard him voice his anger over efforts to spread slavery to more states. But now Mr. Cody only frowned and did not answer the guide.

As Billy, his father, and the guide neared the store, they became the center of attention. At the same time the fierce appearance of the men shocked Billy. Their pants legs were tucked inside high boots, and they glanced suspiciously from under wide-brimmed hats. All carried revolvers in their belts, and some had hunting knives sticking out of their boot tops.

This is the Wild West, for sure, Billy thought. We won't have to look any farther.

The guide greeted several of the men, and then he and Mr. Cody went into the store to meet the owner. Billy remained outside, standing guard over the wagonload of goods. He did not risk getting into conversation with the men. Only after he resumed the journey, half an hour later, did he breathe easily again.

The next day the three reached the Kickapoo Indian reservation. After giving the chief a blanket as a gift, Mr. Cody began to trade with the braves. In exchange for his stock of cloth, sugar, coffee,

The guide and Billy's father became the center of attention

blankets, and tobacco he accepted bundles of furs that the Indians had trapped.

While his father was busy, Billy roamed about the agency making friends with the young Indians. They ran foot races, wrestled, and shot bows and arrows. Through hand signs and much waving of arms, the paleface and the redskin boys made themselves understood.

Billy had the most fun riding Indian ponies, and his skill brought grunts of surprise from the warriors. None of the Indian boys could match his handling of the wildest mounts.

His business finished, Mr. Cody arranged to leave his wagon at the agency while he, Billy, and the guide began to hunt for a homestead.

During the next few days, the three rode over mile after mile of the Kansas plains. To Billy, all of it was perfect. There was more game than he'd ever seen in Iowa, and no fences barred the way. A cabin was a rare sight indeed.

Mr. Cody was more particular. He wanted a stretch of land well watered, sheltered from winter storms, and rich enough to grow good crops. He would make up his mind only when he had seen the best the region offered.

Mr. Cody noted that Billy was growing tired of the constant riding. So, on the evening of the third day, he said, "You stay in camp tomorrow morning and sleep, Billy. The guide and I will look around some more and come back for you." Billy agreed readily.

Next morning he was still sound asleep when the others left at daybreak. The sun was high when he finally stirred in his blankets. He stretched lazily and looked around for Turk, but even he was gone. Billy decided the dog had tired of waiting for him and trotted off after Mr. Cody.

Billy's glance swung out beyond the campsite. With a start, he saw that someone was saddling his horse.

Sitting up quickly, he became aware that the man was an Indian. The brave's scrawny pony stood at one side, his head hanging listlessly.

Grabbing his rifle, Billy called, "Hey, leave that horse alone."

The Indian paid no attention to him, acting as though he hadn't heard. He lifted himself into the saddle and only then glanced up. "Swap ponies," he said. "Me ride paleface boy's pony—paleface ride mine."

Billy became more alarmed than ever. He moved cautiously toward the brave, carrying his rifle. "I can't trade," he said. "That isn't my horse. I mean, I borrowed it. Get off."

The Indian swung his rifle toward Billy to show that he was armed. "Is paleface boy fool?"

Billy checked himself. Would the Indian shoot him? Still, he could not allow Uncle Elijah's horse to be stolen. He took another step forward and called again, "If you don't get off that horse, I'll——"

Surprisingly, the Indian leaped from the horse, threw himself upon his own pony, and galloped from the camp.

Relieved but much more amazed by the brave's action, Billy stared after him. He muttered, "Well, I guess I scared——"

Just then he saw another rider loping toward him. It was the guide, returning to camp alone. Billy now knew why the brave had changed his mind. He began to feel a little meek.

A minute later the guide rode up and said, "Come on, Billy. We've found the place your father wants. I reckon you'll like it, too."

The spot Isaac Cody had picked was in the Salt Creek valley, a rich blue-grass region sheltered by a ring of hills. The trail to Salt Lake passed through the valley, and, as Billy looked, he could see a wagon train crawling over the rim.

"Say, this is all right," he exclaimed. "Only, we'll be pretty close to Rively's trading post, won't we?"

"Not much more than two miles," the guide said, with a hint of disapproval. "It's almost like living in town."

They found Mr. Cody marking off his claim. At its

center, beside a bend in Salt Creek, stood a grove of willow and cottonwood trees. Billy didn't have to be told that his father had picked this spot for their house, barn, and corral.

Mr. Cody rode toward Billy and the guide. Lean and tall, he had the ruddy look of an outdoor man. His eyes were bright with hope and eagerness and more alive than Billy had ever seen them.

"We'll put up a one-room shed over there," he said, pointing. "It will give us a roof while we build a solid log cabin under those cottonwoods. Our permanent home will have to be double size, for our big family," he added with a grin.

His plans made, Mr. Cody lost no time. After picking up the trading wagon, the three returned to Weston. Before another week passed, the Codys were living in their first Kansas home, a rough drafty cabin that served them until their larger log house was finished.

Chapter 3

A FIGHT WITH A PANTHER

As the only boy of the family, Billy Cody accepted his parents' trust and the duties that came his way with a cheerful spirit. Although slender, his wiry strength and fearlessness led him to undertake any job his father felt he could manage.

An endless amount of work was needed to make a new farm out of the raw Kansas homestead, and Billy had few idle moments. He was rarely indoors except to eat meals and sleep.

His older sisters, Martha and Julia, looked after Eliza, Helen, and Mary, the smallest of the Cody children. Mrs. Cody was frail and delicate and needed the girls' help to run her large household.

Billy's older brother Samuel had been fatally injured in an accident the year before the family left for the West. A skilled rider, he delighted in riding spirited horses. But one day, he lost control of a very unruly one. The horse reared and threw Samuel off. Then it fell on him and crushed him.

Mrs. Cody's grief for her fourteen-year-old son weakened her already strained health. Her wish to move from the scene of the tragedy was one of the reasons for the Codys' westward journey.

The best part of Billy's day was the time allowed him to hunt. His skill with a rifle was already so sharp that the family table was never without game. Turk was Billy's willing companion on these hunting trips, but sometimes he had to stay behind to guard the younger children.

One day, after hunting alone, Billy returned home with a pair of wild turkeys. He found his mother alarmed by the absence of his two youngest sisters.

"Oh, Billy, Helen and Eliza have wandered away," she said. "I suppose they're picking flowers but I'm so worried. They've been gone for an hour. Go look for them, please."

"All right, Mother. But Turk must be with them. They'll be all right. I'll find them."

Reloading his rifle, Billy started walking toward a wooded hillside half a mile away. Now and then he whistled sharply to call Turk. At last he heard an answering bark. It was faint, yet pitched in a key that signaled trouble.

Starting to run, Billy soon heard the sounds of a fierce struggle in the woods. Turk was battling some animal and his cries of pain told Billy that he was getting the worst of the fight.

Almost out of breath, Billy reached the edge of the woods in time to see a black panther make another

Turk was battling some wild creature

lunge at the dog. The animal lashed at Turk with its paw, raking the dog's head. The blow knocked him to one side and stunned him.

Instantly Billy threw his rifle to his shoulder and fired. The panther fell dead with a bullet through its heart.

Just then a mound of leaves and brush near the slain animal burst apart and two small girls, wailing with fright, ran to Billy and threw themselves upon him.

"Why, 'Liza . . . Helen, what happened?" Billy asked. "How did you——"

Eliza began to stammer, "Oh, Billy, we . . . the panther . . . Turk . . . Oh, Billy!"

"You're all right now," Billy said soothingly. "Don't cry. Nothing will happen to you."

As soon as he had checked the girls' fright, Billy knelt beside Turk. The dog whined feebly as Billy examined his wounds.

He was relieved to see that, except for deep scratches, Turk had not been badly hurt.

"You're a good dog," Billy said. "Yes, sir, a good dog."

After resting for a few minutes, Turk crawled to his feet. Slowly Billy, his sisters, and Turk started for home. On the way, the girls told how they had been picking flowers in the woods when they heard the panther's frightening scream.

Turk had nudged them into a shallow pit and pawed leaves over them until they were hidden. As the big cat crept closer, the dog stood guard. When the animal pounced at the girls, Turk leaped into its path and fought until Billy's shot ended the battle.

"You'd better pick flowers closer to home after this," Billy warned. "Mother will be sick when she hears what almost happened to you. It's a good thing Turk is big and strong or he could never have saved you."

"You saved us, Billy," Helen said.

"I only shot the panther," Billy said. "Turk is the one that fought him."

Some days later, Billy was sent to Rively's trading post for a bag of flour. On the way he passed a wagon train hauling Army supplies. Then he came upon a large party of emigrants. Billy realized that the trail through Salt Creek valley was becoming more traveled with each passing week.

At the trading post, he found the usual crowd of settlers, bullwhackers, and soldiers as well as a few trappers back from the mountains. He had overcome his first mistrust about meeting them and now enjoyed listening to their stories of adventure, daring, hardship, and fights with Indians.

Sometimes, though, they argued angrily about whether Missouri and Kansas should be free or slave states. Billy noticed that on their trips to the store his father avoided taking part in these debates.

This day Billy had been at the post only a short time when a store clerk said to him, "A young fellow named Horace Billings was in today asking about your father, Billy. He's a wild one . . . ran away from home, rode in a circus, broke broncos, and I don't know what all. He says Isaac Cody is his uncle. That would make you his cousin."

"Oh, yes, I've heard of Horace but I've never seen him," Billy said. "Is he still here?"

"He probably is." The clerk glanced toward the door as a stocky young man entered. "There he is now." The clerk beckoned and called, "Come over here, Billings. This is one of the Codys you've been asking about."

Billy looked at the dark-faced man walking toward him. His step was light and he moved with the easy grace of an Indian. His smile was quick and friendly.

When Billy was introduced, Horace said, "Well, well, so you're Isaac Cody's son. I'm happy to meet you, cousin."

As Billy talked with Horace, he learned that his cousin had spent the past winter trapping furs in the Wyoming mountains. Now he was undertaking a job for the Army. The commander at Fort Leavenworth had hired him to round up a herd of horses that had stampeded and headed for the plains. He was just leaving to begin the search.

"Why don't you stop at our farm tonight?" Billy invited. "It's on your way. My family will be glad to see you."

"All right, I will," Horace said promptly. "Thank you very much."

Billy liked his cousin immensely. To every question that Billy put to him, Horace had the answer. He knew all corners of the West, and his experiences with wild animals and Indians were breath-taking.

One thing puzzled him. Horace gave close attention to how Billy sat in his saddle and how he handled his horse. But he made no comment.

Once he asked, "How are you with a rifle, Billy?"

For answer, Billy raised his gun quickly and fired at a prairie chicken flying past a stone's throw away. The bird dropped dead on the trail.

"Umm," Horace muttered. Billy stopped to pick up the bird. Horace appeared more thoughtful during the rest of the ride.

The Codys greeted Horace warmly and spent the evening visiting with him. At one point he said, "I wish I had someone with me on my horse hunt. I'll collect ten dollars for every horse I catch and can pay a helper something. Would you allow Billy to go along?"

Billy caught his breath. He hadn't given the idea a thought—it was too much to hope for. But now that Horace had brought it up, he sat as one stunned. Oh, if he could only——

Horace went on, "Billy certainly knows how to manage horses and when it comes to shooting——" He smiled at his young cousin. "I'd like to teach him how to live on the plains, how to read signs, follow a trail, and learn the habits of wild animals. Living out here in the West, Billy should know all he can about it."

Billy saw his father and mother exchange glances and noted the reluctance in his mother's eyes. But after a minute Mr. Cody nodded.

"It would be a good thing for Billy, no doubt. He will never have a better chance to learn how to take care of himself. Yes, Horace, if you want to bother with him, he may go."

Turning to Billy, he added, "Do you want to, son?"

Billy's breath came out in a gasp. "Oh . . . oh, yes, father. I should say I do. I'd rather do that than anything!"

Horace laughed in his easy manner. "Fine. If he just does as I tell him, we'll get along first rate. Can you be ready by sunup, Billy?"

"I can be ready in five minutes," Billy said. "I'm ready right now."

Chapter 4

THE ATTACK

Billy Cody studied the hoof marks for another minute. He frowned as he tried to separate the dozens of footprints that scarred the soft earth around the waterhole on the Kansas plain. When he glanced up, he saw Horace Billings smiling at his puzzled expression.

"Well, Billy, what do you make of them?" Horace asked.

"I can tell the buffalo tracks from the horse trail, of course, but. . . ." Billy stopped to look at the ground again. "How do you know which are Indian ponies and which are Army horses?"

His cousin moved away from the waterhole. Pointing to several prints in front of him, he said, "Those are made by ponies. If you'll look close, you'll see they're a little smaller than the others. And they carried riders. The prints are deeper because of the extra weight."

"The horse trail is freshest," Billy noted.

"We can be thankful for that," Horace went on. "The Indians passed along here a day ago and the horses we're trailing stopped this morning. If it had been the other way around, the braves would be after our horses this minute. Come on, Billy, we have work to do."

The trail led steadily westward, and night came without Billy and Horace catching sight of the Army mounts. As they made camp, Horace said they would catch up with the horse herd soon.

Each day brought new wonders and delights to Billy. The vast sweep of the rolling plain, the breeze against his face, the warm sun, the feeling of freedom such as he'd never experienced before, filled him with love for the outdoor life Horace was teaching him.

He listened carefully to all that his cousin told him about tracking animals and reading trail signs. He began to note landmarks—an unusual rock, a certain hill, a clump of trees, or a shallow river—so that if need be, he could find his way back and not become lost.

Horace's skill over a campfire surprised Billy. He learned how to roast strips of meat by holding them on the end of a stick over a blaze. Dough wrapped around another stick could be baked into bread by the same method.

Under Horace's teaching, Billy learned the knack of roping a horse with a lasso. Trying to become expert, he practiced every evening until darkness stopped him.

Billy gazed in amazement at the great herds of buffalo that moved ceaselessly across the plains. Once a herd thundered by in a wild stampede, sending up a great cloud of dust and causing the earth to shake.

"It would be fun to hunt buffalo, Horace," Billy suggested.

"Sure it would," his cousin said, "but right now our business is to hunt horses."

Before another day passed, they came upon the herd grazing in the thick tangle of a river bottom. Making a wide sweep around the horses to cut off their flight to the west, Billy and Horace tried to drive the animals away from the river. The herd split up, half of it breaking across the stream and galloping away. The two riders had all they could do to hold their bunch from joining the runaways.

Horace was disappointed. He and Billy drove their captives into a little pocket among some hills a mile from the river.

"I'll have to find a cavalry patrol to take these horses off our hands," Horace said. "Then we can go on and round up the others. I'll have to leave you here to watch this bunch until I get back. Do you think you can do that?"

"Oh, sure," Billy said, although he wasn't so sure. He could not let Horace think he had any fear.

Horace came across a squad of soldiers sooner than he had expected to. He brought them back to where

40

Billy was waiting. It was dark then, and the troopers shared the horse hunters' camp for the night. This was Billy's first contact with the rough and daring men who policed the plains. He was drawn to them by their good humor and generosity.

Early the next morning, Billy and Horace left them to take up the chase of the missing mounts. Two more weeks passed before they were able to bring the herd into Fort Leavenworth.

While Horace collected his pay from the quartermaster, Billy looked into the barracks and stables and watched the cavalrymen drill. He had a hard time deciding whether he wanted to be a soldier or a hunter and trapper like Horace.

When his cousin rejoined Billy, he said, "Now I'll deliver you home, partner."

"Oh, you don't have to do that," Billy protested. "I know the way. Of course, we'd like to have you visit us again."

He stopped when Horace dropped a small bag into his hands. It was so heavy he almost dropped it. "What's this?" Billy asked.

"Your wages," said Horace. Billy opened the bag and gasped. He poured out the large silver coins and counted them.

"Twenty-five dollars!" he exclaimed. "Oh, Horace, that's too much. I never had money before."

"You earned it," Horace said. With a grin he

added, "Come on. I'll have to keep an eye on you or you might spend it."

As they rode toward the Cody farm, Billy said, "I never had so much fun, Horace. I can't thank you enough for taking me along."

Horace smiled. "If you can call roughing it out here fun, you're going to be a real plainsman."

"Oh, do you think so? I guess I'd rather be that than anything else."

As soon as he reached home, Billy leaped from his horse and ran into the cabin. Before saying a word, he thrust his wages into his mother's hands. "Here, Mother, I earned this for you."

Mrs. Cody hugged Billy and said, "Oh, son, we're so happy to have you back."

She fingered the bag of coins and asked, "What's this?" Before she could examine it, Billy's sisters swarmed upon him, squealing their delight over their brother's return.

Soon Mr. Cody and Horace joined the happy group. The excitement lasted many minutes, and Billy noticed his mother's eyes glistening with joy and pride.

At last Horace Billings had a chance to speak. "I hope I haven't spoiled Billy. He talks as though farming isn't going to appeal to him much longer. He was a big help to me."

"Billy is pretty young to think of living your kind

of life, Horace," Mr. Cody said. "But I'm glad he had this chance to learn how to take care of himself away from home."

After spending the night with the Codys, Horace left to prepare for another winter of trapping in the mountains. Billy took up his farm duties again, but it was hard to keep his eyes off the trail where wagon trains pushed westward in never-ending columns.

Settlers were taking up homesteads in the neighborhood and each week more cabins dotted the plains. As he worked at his many chores, Billy noticed that his father appeared troubled and uneasy. He puzzled over it but thought it best not to ask questions. He was sure the farm was everything his parents had hoped for and yet some vague worry had settled over the household.

The weeks ran into months for Billy. Winter gave him more time to hunt and to visit the Kickapoo reservation. He began to learn some Indian words and before long was able to understand the chatter of his redskin friends.

The snow halted wagon travel over the plains, but the trains appeared again as soon as the grass was long enough to feed the horses and oxen.

One summer day in 1855, Billy and his father drove in the farm wagon to Rively's store. An unusually large crowd had gathered there, many of them newcomers from Missouri. Mr. Cody sought to avoid them by paying no heed to their loud talk. Billy heard the words "slavery" and "free soil" spoken often.

One of the men finally placed himself before Mr. Cody. The others turned to watch what would happen.

"Cody, we haven't heard you speak up on this slavery question," the man said. "We want all the backing we can get against this free soil gang trying to keep us out of Kansas. If you're for us, we want to hear you say so."

He pulled a box around and added, "All right, Cody. Step up and give us your speech."

Billy saw his father's face grow pale. Yet he did not hesitate to climb upon the box and face the crowd. He paused for a minute to control himself.

"Gentlemen," he began, "I seek no quarrel with you, but you are wrong if you think that I will help your scheme. Slavery is a cruel, wicked system. I have always been against it and I always will be. If slavery sinks its roots into this free soil, it will be a curse to Kansas. That, gentlemen, is where I stand."

There was a moment of stunned silence. Then the crowd gave a bellow of rage. Shouts of "Kill him!" "Lynch him!" rang out. Like a wave, the mob closed around Mr. Cody.

With growing alarm, Billy saw the angry faces and listened to the terrifying words. He stood rooted,

"Look out, Father!" Billy shouted

unable to move. Then he saw a man jerk a hunting knife from his boot and move in.

"Look out, Father!" Billy shouted. The warning came too late. An arm lifted high, the sun glinted on steel. A second later the sharp blade tore into Mr. Cody's chest. With a groan of agony, he slumped from the box.

Billy sprang forward to break his father's fall. He caught an arm but could not prevent him from dropping all the way to the ground.

"Fath . . . Father," Billy stammered. "Can . . . can you speak to me?"

Chapter 5

A RIDE FOR LIFE

Numb with horror, Billy found it hard to breathe. Anxiously, he gazed down at his father's face, searching for a hint of life. The eyes were closed, and a deep pallor replaced the ruddy color of Mr. Cody's cheeks.

A voice above Billy said, "Here, boy, let us get him away."

A hand pushed Billy aside gently. Two men stooped to pick up his father. He recognized one as Mr. Hathaway, a neighbor in Salt Creek valley. They carried Isaac Cody into Rively's store.

To follow, Billy had to force life into his sluggish legs. Glancing around for the first time, he saw that the mob had slunk away. Some of the men were riding off as fast as their horses could carry them.

Billy entered the store and pushed himself to Mr. Hathaway's side. The neighbor was bending over Mr. Cody, wiping the knife wound with a wet cloth.

To his unbounded relief, Billy saw that his father's eyes were open. He wasn't dead, after all! Billy felt like weeping for joy, but he controlled himself.

His father's glance swung to him. "You . . .

46

you're all right, son?" he whispered. "They didn't harm you?"

"Sure . . . sure, I'm all right."

"Don't talk, Cody," Mr. Hathaway said. "Save your strength." He dabbed at the wound. "It's a bad cut, but it missed your heart. We'll put you in your wagon and take you home. The missus will know what to do for you."

Billy sat beside his father in the wagon box while Mr. Hathaway drove the team. He groaned with his parent at every jolt in the rough road. He thought the ride would never end.

After her first panic at the sight of her injured husband, Mary Cody began to nurse him calmly.

"I always feared that this would happen, Isaac," she said. "Oh, those terrible men—— I'm afraid this is not the end of our trouble."

In the days that followed, Mr. Cody regained his strength slowly. Billy worked harder than ever to keep up with the farm chores. Word brought by neighbors told of the mob's intention to strike again, this time at the Cody home.

Now and then, Billy rode to Rively's to buy food but also to keep an eye on the crowd. What he learned one day sent him racing home to warn his father. The gang was coming that night.

Although far from well, Mr. Cody ran from the cabin and hid in a cornfield. A party of horsemen, armed with revolvers and rifles, soon rode into the yard. They searched the house and barn in vain.

Angered by their failure to find Mr. Cody, they left with a threat. "He's around here somewhere and we'll get him. The next time we'll finish the job. We'll be back."

After the riders left, Billy carried food and blankets to his father, who continued to hide for several days. But it was clear to the family that this could not go on.

Mrs. Cody urged her husband, "Isaac, your life is in danger here. You must leave until this question of slavery is settled."

"Ah, Mary, I fear that will not be soon," Mr. Cody said. "But I know I cannot remain here. It is with a heavy heart that I go." He turned to Billy and put a hand on his shoulder. "Son, until I return, you must be the head of the house."

"I'll look after Mother and the girls," he said quickly. "I'll take care of them."

"It is a heavy duty for one so young, but I have every faith in you."

That night Mr. Cody rode off, first taking refuge in Leavenworth and later joining friends who believed as he did that Kansas must not become a slave state.

The dispute flared into bitter hates during the passing weeks. Men shot and killed each other, mobs hanged innocent victims, farm buildings were burned. Parts of Kansas were in a state of war. Several times night riders alarmed the Cody household as they hunted for Billy's father.

To earn money needed by his family, Billy herded horses and oxen for two months at the supply depot of the government freight company. Proudly he brought home his wages to his mother.

While Mr. Cody was away, a son Charles was born. Happy over having a brother again, Billy was more resolved than ever to live up to his father's trust and hopes.

A year passed before Mr. Cody, still suffering from his knife wound, returned home. But word of his arrival reached his enemies, and when new attempts were made to kill him, he left again.

This time he sought safety at a place called Grasshopper Falls, thirty-five miles west of Fort Leavenworth, where he built a sawmill. Occasionally he risked a night ride home to visit his family, but he was never free of the danger of capture and death.

On the day Mr. Cody planned one of his secret trips, Billy became ill with a cold and fever. His mother sent him to bed. "You've been working too hard, Billy. The rest will do you good."

Too weak to argue, he went meekly to his bedroom.

Just before noon, Mr. Hathaway came to the

Cody farm with alarming news. "The gang has heard Isaac plans to ride here tonight, Mrs. Cody," he said excitedly. "They're setting a trap for him at Big Stranger Creek. If he starts out, he'll be killed."

"Oh, this is terrible," Mary Cody said, dread flashing over her face. "I wish someone could stop Isaac."

Billy, listening from his bedroom, forced himself to his feet. Staggering from weakness, he joined his mother and Mr. Hathaway. "I'll ride to Father and warn him."

"Oh, no, Billy," Mary Cody protested. "You are much too ill. You have a fever. That long ride will be the death of you."

"Father is in danger," Billy said stoutly. "He would come to me if I needed help. It is my place to ride to him." He turned to his two older sisters. "Julia, Martha, please saddle my horse. I'll be ready in a minute."

Mrs. Cody continued to object to Billy's rash plan but could not change his mind. When he tried to mount his horse, his sisters had fairly to lift him into his saddle.

His face cooled by the breeze, Billy forgot his illness as he started the thirty-mile ride. He had to reach the sawmill before dark to deliver his warning in time.

Billy knew he'd face his greatest danger halfway

to the mill, where the trail crossed Big Stranger Creek. There brush and trees in the narrow valley offered a thick cover for anyone planning an ambush.

For an hour, he rode at a fast pace. As he approached the creek, he slowed to a walk, hoping to escape the notice of anyone lurking there. His horse was in the water when he saw a man peering over a clump of brush. The man shouted, "Hey, there, where're you—— It's the Cody boy! Stop, boy! Stop or we'll shoot."

Billy jammed his heels into the horse's flanks. The animal leaped forward, breaking into a gallop.

A rifle shot, then a second, sounded behind Billy. The bullets swished past his head. He heard shouts and the thud of hoofs as horses charged from their hiding place.

Glancing back, Billy saw half a dozen horsemen begin to chase him.

Pressing himself flat against his mount, he sped up the creek valley, skimmed over a rise, and struck out across a grass-covered flat. The trail led over a hill and through a thicket.

The pursuing horses were fresh; Billy's was beginning to tire from its long run. But he coaxed and pleaded for more speed. The six riders crowded closer upon him.

Clouds hung low over the plain, casting a heavy gloom around Billy. A flash of lightning, followed

"Don't leave, Father. There's a gang waiting to shoot you."

instantly by a thunderous crash, loosed the storm.
Rain poured down in sweeping sheets, soaking him
before he had ridden a hundred yards.

The trail turned to mud and water, but Billy
pressed on without letup. He could not tell how long
he struggled against the cold rain, but finally the
thunder slackened and the clouds lifted.

Billy looked back. His pursuers were no longer in
sight. Hope filled him again.

Then a chill shook him. Thoroughly drenched, he
felt the return of his fever and he grew so weak he

could hardly hold himself in the saddle. But he gave no thought of stopping now.

He reached the sawmill just as his father led a horse from the stable. Rushing up to his astonished parent, Billy cried, "Don't leave, Father. There's a gang waiting to shoot you. You must not start out——"

Then everything went black. Billy slid off his horse into his father's arms.

Chapter 6

A MAN'S JOB FOR BILLY

When Billy regained his senses, he found himself abed in a little cabin near the sawmill. His father sat beside the bunk, wiping Billy's hot face with a wet cloth.

Grinning up weakly, Billy said, "I guess . . . I must have passed out a minute ago."

"That was yesterday, Billy."

"Yesterday! Where, what——"

"You've been pretty sick, but your fever has broken," his father said. "You just stay quiet for a few days and you'll be all right."

"We can't stay here, Father. The gang——"

"They're a cowardly bunch and won't risk coming here while my workmen are around." Mr. Cody wiped Billy's face again. "You did a brave thing, son, by riding so far to warn me. A grown person might have failed to get through as you did. I'm proud of you."

Billy settled back happily and was soon asleep again. Two days later he was well enough to get up

54

and his father decided it was time to leave the saw-mill.

"Tonight we'll ride to Lawrence, where the Free Soil people have a meeting place," he said. "From there we'll find a way to send you home."

Although small, Lawrence was a busy village working to keep slavery out of Kansas. The leaders asked Mr. Cody to go East to urge more Free Soil people to settle in Kansas. Knowing that he was not safe at home, Mr. Cody left for Ohio to work for the cause.

A day or two later, Billy had a chance to leave Lawrence with two men going to Fort Leavenworth. From there he rode home in an hour.

His safe arrival ended his mother's worry over him and her husband. A letter his father had written, and delivered by Billy, explained his trip to the East.

"Oh, I'm so glad that you are back," Mrs. Cody said. "These days without word from you and Father have made me ill."

The weeks passed swiftly for Billy. There was work every day, but he found time to meet many wagon bosses and teamsters as they came and went from the freight depot at Fort Leavenworth. He was a welcome visitor. Their camps became a school in which he learned about horses, oxen, and life on the western trails.

At home, he engaged his sisters and Turk in his

wild and lively Indian wars, stagecoach holdups, soldier and cowboy games. He scalped their dolls, frightened them with jack-o'-lanterns and plagued them in a dozen ways. Although his teasing knew no limit, his sisters and young brother adored him and were willing victims of his play.

When a school was finally started in Salt Creek valley, Billy attended with his older sisters. He fought Stephen Gobel, the school bully, and took a keen interest in Mary Hyatt, a young and pretty pupil. But his classroom days were limited, and he proved a better student in the world of horses, cattle, and wagon trains.

Mr. Cody came home now and then for short periods, but his enemies gave him no peace. His life was in constant danger, and the knife wound he had suffered began to affect his lung. Forced to his bed at last, he died in April, 1857.

Thus at the age of eleven, Billy Cody became the head of the family. Upon him fell the duty of providing for his mother, five sisters, and brother Charlie. He faced the task without a thought that it was too great for him.

"Mother, I must get a job and earn some money," he said. "I'll ask Uncle Alec to give me work."

"Uncle Alec?" Mrs. Cody said. "You have no Uncle Alec."

"Well, I mean Mr. Majors, who hires men for the

wagon trains hauling Army supplies. All the young fellows around Leavenworth call him Uncle Alec because . . . well, he's like an uncle to us. I hope he'll let me go to Kearney or even to Fort Laramie with one of his trains."

"But Billy, you're too young for that," his mother said. "That is work for grown men, not boys. Besides, it would take you too far from home. You'd be gone for weeks and weeks. And it's too dangerous. Think of all the Indians and buffalo and outlaws."

"There's nothing to be afraid of, Mother," Billy said. "Not when I'll be with a whole crowd of bullwhackers on the trail. They don't let Indians and outlaws stop them. I'll be as safe as I am here, almost. It's my best chance of getting work. You'll let me talk to Mr. Majors, won't you?"

Mrs. Cody sighed. "Well, you go see what he says. But don't be disappointed if he says no. You're still very young, remember."

Happily, Billy donned his buckskin shirt, tucked his pants legs inside his boot tops and buckled his father's revolver around his waist. Sure now that he looked fit for the trail, he rode off to the Russell, Majors & Waddell supply depot at Fort Leavenworth. He found Alec Majors busy in his office.

Eager to have his business settled at once, Billy blurted out his plea, "Uncle Alec, please give me a job with a wagon train. I need work. My father . . .

I have to take his place and earn money for my mother. You'll find a place for me, won't you?"

Alec Majors smiled at his eager visitor. "Well, Billy, what do you expect to do around a wagon train?"

"Oh, I can ride and shoot and . . . and herd live-stock. I don't care what it is, just so I can work for you."

"I've seen you handle horses and I've heard about your shooting," Mr. Majors said. "I hardly think you'll do just yet as a bullwhacker, though," he added with a smile. Then he became serious. "Will your mother allow you to leave home? Does she know about your coming here?"

"Oh, yes, sir. She wasn't very sure you'd hire me, but you know, Uncle Alec, this means everything. I have to work now and look after my family."

Billy saw Uncle Alec's glance soften and he took hope. "It's fine of you, Billy, to want to help your mother," Mr. Majors said. "I like your spirit." He thought for a minute. "Do you know what a wagon train 'extra' does?"

"He . . . does he help out wherever he can? Like run errands for the wagon boss?"

"Not only that, but any other chore that comes along. Rustle wood for the cook, fetch water, ride herd on the extra steers. Would you care for work like that?"

"Yes, sir! I'll do anything."

"All right. If you make good, I'll pay you a man's wages, forty dollars a month. In the morning, I'm sending out Frank and Bill McCarthy with a few wagons and a big herd of cattle. They and their crew will take the beef to the soldiers beyond Fort Laramie. You can go with them."

"Oh, thank you, Uncle Alec." Billy knew the McCarthy brothers. They were among Majors's most trusted wagon bosses. Billy felt fortunate indeed to be attached to their outfit.

Mr. Majors took a sheet of paper from a desk drawer. "Everyone I hire has to sign this pledge, Billy. Do you know about the pledge?"

"Yes, but I've never seen one."

"Let me read it to you," Mr. Majors said. He paused a moment to write Billy's name in a blank space and began, "I, William Frederick Cody, do hereby swear before the Great and Living God, that while I am in the employ of Russell, Majors & Waddell, I will not use profane language, will not get drunk, will not gamble, will not quarrel with any other employee of the firm; that I will not abuse nor neglect the animals and that I will conduct myself honestly, be faithful to my duties and so direct all my acts as will win the confidence of my employers. So help me God."

"I'll promise all that," Billy said.

Mr. Majors gave his new employee a small Bible, as he did to all the men he hired. Billy tucked it into his shirt pocket and shook Mr. Majors's outstretched hand. "Come back before dark, Billy. Your outfit starts out early in the morning."

Billy rode home happily to tell of his success. His mother voiced her relief when she learned of the pledge he had signed.

"I'm so glad that you're working for a good man like Mr. Majors," she said. "Now you must live up to your promise, Billy. And do be careful . . . the Indians. They worry me so."

Billy had a hard time escaping from his clamoring sisters who were in tears over his leaving home. Even little Charlie joined in the hubbub, although too young to know the reason for it.

That night in May, 1857, Billy slept under a wagon, as did the rest of McCarthys' crew. Up at daybreak, he took hold of his every duty as though the job of breaking camp was his alone.

As soon as breakfast was out of the way, he helped the bullwhackers bring up and yoke their oxen. By the time Frank McCarthy shouted the order "Stretch out!" he had proved that he wanted favors from no one.

Once the wagons were rolling ahead of the cattle, Billy took his place with the herders. Until noon, the train plodded on steadily. After a two-hour rest, the

They halted to make camp for the night

outfit resumed its march and then halted in the late afternoon to make camp for the night.

After the wagons were drawn into a tight corral, the animals were allowed to graze nearby. During the night, Billy took his turn riding around the sleeping cattle.

The gathering of the trail veterans around the campfires gave Billy boundless joy. He never tired of their stories of adventure and courage. He was treated as a man among men, and he knew that he would never again be satisfied to live the quiet life of either city or farm.

The train stopped briefly at Fort Kearney in Nebraska. The crude buildings of the Army post beside the North Platte River disappointed Billy. The fort lacked even a trace of the dash and polish he had grown used to at Leavenworth.

The wagons and cattle herd reached Plum Creek, thirty-five miles west of Kearney, one day at noon. Three of the herders stood watch over the grazing animals while the rest of the crew napped under the corralled wagons. After helping the cook clean up the dinner dishes, Billy stretched out beside Frank McCarthy.

The unexpected sound of gunfire awoke Billy. By the time he had brushed the fog from his brain, the wagon boss was shouting, "Indians, boys. The red-skins have jumped us."

Billy stumbled to his feet. He gazed toward the animals but saw nothing of the three herders. He caught a glimpse of a dozen mounted braves charging upon the corral.

"Here they come, boys," Frank McCarthy shouted. "Grab your guns. Let 'em have it."

Chapter 7

THE INDIAN RAID

Seizing his rifle, Billy ran across the corral to meet the onrushing Indians. He flung himself to the ground under a wagon, pressing himself against a wheel. On either side of him were stretched McCarthy's bull-whackers and cattle herders, their guns propped upon wheel spokes and wagon tongues.

"Not yet," Frank McCarthy warned. "Hold your fire, boys."

Trembling despite his best efforts to steady his arms, Billy waited in a sweat of terror. His chest was so tight every breath gave him pain.

Why didn't McCarthy let them—— In another moment the howling riders would sweep over the corral. Their arrows were already zipping through the canvas tops and clattering against wagon boxes.

"Now!" McCarthy said. He spoke in a low steady voice. Its calmness drove away a bit of Billy's panic.

The crash of a dozen rifle shots burst around Billy. The smoke of his own gun curled over him and blended with that of the others, forming a milky

Billy flung himself under a wagon and rested his rifle on the spoke of a wheel

screen. The acrid bite of burned gunpowder stung his nostrils.

A grunt of pain drew Billy's attention to a bull-whacker he knew only as Luke, who was tugging at an arrow in his chest. No one paid any heed to him.

After quickly reloading his rifle, Billy joined his

64

crewmates in another volley. The warriors drew out of range but continued their shrill war cries.

The sound of running animals broke across the plain and Billy saw that the train's cattle herd was in a wild stampede. It was clear to him then that some of the attacking Indians were driving off the livestock.

During several minutes of tense waiting, Bill McCarthy crept to the injured bullwhacker and plugged his wound with a piece of cloth. Marveling at Luke's calm acceptance of pain, Billy wondered how he would meet it if a bullet or arrow struck him.

A sharp word from the wagon boss turned his gaze back to the warriors. He saw a score or more braves ride up to join the corral attackers.

With fresh alarm, he noticed the enlarged force bunch up and get ready for another charge.

"They're too many for us," Frank McCarthy said. "Head for the creek, boys . . . get behind the creek bank. We'll lay low and give the redskins anything they ask for."

Crouching as they ran, the wagon crew quit the corral and headed for Plum Creek, a few hundred yards away. Two bullwhackers steadied the injured Luke as they ducked out of the ring of wagons.

Billy found himself beside the cook.

"Those three fellows who were with the cattle . . . I don't see them," Billy said.

"No need looking," the cook said. "The redskins got them."

"Do you mean they're . . . they're dead?"

"Deader than last year's hay crop. And their hair lifted, besides. They're all done herding livestock."

A yell, then a chorus of war whoops, added speed to Billy's legs. Without looking back, he could tell that the braves were aware of the white men's flight. The hoofbeats of their racing ponies sounded dreadfully close.

A flying leap carried him over the bank into shallow water. Spinning around, he threw himself against the sheer earth wall. He stood just high enough to rest his rifle at shoulder level.

The others dropped over the creek bank one by one. By the time Luke slid to the water, the warriors' arrows were flying among the whites.

Billy saw a ragged line of horsemen bearing down upon him and his companions. He fired into the mass and saw a horse rear and throw its rider to the ground.

Then a blast of gunfire roared in his ears as the bullwhackers met the challenge. The solid pack of Indians split and turned aside. For the moment, the assault had been beaten off.

The gunfire stopped as abruptly as it began. Billy glanced around to see that except for the wounded teamster, all the men were on their feet.

Another sound came to him and the little group hugging the creek bank. The wagons' canvas tops were being ripped apart, boxes and barrels tossed to the ground and smashed open. The warriors were looting the train.

Billy heard Frank McCarthy mutter angrily at the Indians. His tone changed suddenly. "Here's our chance to break away, boys. Those redskins will be busy at their fun for a while. We'll work our way down the creek to the Platte River and then try to make it back to Fort Kearney."

"That's a long walk, Frank," one of the bull-whackers said. "A good thirty-five miles, as I reckon it."

"We either walk or stay here and argue with the redskins," the wagon boss said. "We're better off walking."

Under cover of the high bank, the wagon crew started down Plum Creek. In several places water filled the bed and had to be waded. Billy was wet to the shoulders before he had gone a quarter mile.

When the Indians discovered the white men were escaping, they came charging back to renew the fight. After being driven off, they trailed the wagon crew and whenever possible, crept close enough to open fire.

Presently a column of smoke lifted above the

prairie and Billy exclaimed aloud, "They're burning our wagons!"

"That's one of the best things they do," McCarthy said with disgust.

When the men reached the North Platte River, their difficulties increased. Where the current swept against the shore, they found it hard to keep their footing. They dared not leave the water because of the Indians' nearness. The injured Luke could barely keep up with the others.

At one point the river was too deep to wade and Frank McCarthy called a halt. "We'll have to build a raft and push it ahead of us," he said. "It'll keep our guns out of water and give Luke something to rest on."

When at flood stage a few weeks earlier, the Platte had tumbled a dozen or more tree trunks upon the river bank where the men now found themselves. Half a dozen of the crew began to roll several of the smaller logs into the water. Others gathered long lengths of grapevine that grew in a thick tangle back from the stream and used these to bind the logs together.

The raft bobbed in the fast current and seemed likely to break away at any moment. As more and more vines were woven around the logs, however, the float took on a more secure look.

The Indians attacked again while the men worked

on their raft. After a sharp exchange of fire, they pulled back but remained close enough to be a constant menace.

When the crude float was finished, Luke was boosted aboard. Frank turned to Billy. "How about it, boy? Tuckered out and want to ride with Luke?"

"No," said Billy stoutly. "I'm all right."

"Good boy," said Frank. "Watch out now and don't drop behind. It'll be dark in another hour and it'll be harder to see the redskins."

Soaked to the chin, Billy felt the night's chill gnaw into him. Hunger brought another ache, but he fought back every groan of complaint that crowded his lips. The others were pushing on without a sign of weakness and so would he.

The men were still several miles from Fort Kearney at dawn. As daylight colored the dry plains, anxious eyes scanned them for danger.

"They're gone," Frank McCarthy said at last. "We're close to the fort and they won't give us any more trouble."

Walking became easier as the men left the river, but Billy's legs dragged as though burdened with chains. The warm sun in his face stirred him with fresh energy, but even so he stumbled as he entered the gate of the fort.

Frank McCarthy caught his arm and kept him from falling. "Well, Bill, you played a man's part in our little set-to with the redskins. You've got more grit than I expected to find in a young shaver. You can work for me any time."

Bill! Frank McCarthy had called him Bill! Not the kid name, Billy, that made him feel small and child-like.

He grinned up at the wagon boss. He was too weak and tired to do more than that.

McCarthy's story of the Indian attack brought quick action at the fort. While the wagon crew ate a big breakfast, the post commander called out two companies of soldiers to chase the warriors. The McCarthy brothers and their bullwhackers rode with the troops.

Bill asked to go along, but the wagon boss told him he was not needed. Barely able to keep awake, he did not argue with Frank.

The soldiers found only the burned corral and the bodies of the three herders at the wagon camp. The Indians, driving their stolen cattle, were trailed up Plum Creek toward the Republican River. Only a few animals were found on the all-day hunt. The braves had escaped with most of the wagon train's herd.

McCarthy's men remained at Fort Kearney until they could join an empty train returning to Fort Leavenworth. After reaching there, Bill Cody reported to Alec Majors.

"I'm sorry we lost our wagon train," he said. "I wish I could have done something—— You'll give me another chance, won't you?"

Mr. Majors smiled at his young employee. "Frank McCarthy tells me that you were as cool as an old-timer in the Indian fight, Billy. I was glad to hear it; the trail is no place for a fellow who scares easily. I was sure you were made of the right stuff, otherwise I'd never have hired you. We'll have another job for you, Billy."

"Thanks, Uncle Alec." He added quickly, "Frank McCarthy calls me Bill now—after that Indian fight."

Mr. Majors appeared puzzled for a moment and then broke into a hearty laugh. "He's right. You've outgrown Billy and from now on you're Bill Cody to all of us."

Bill's grin was one of pride and pleasure. Before he could speak, Mr. Majors said, "Before long, we'll be sending a train of supplies to General Johnston's troops in Utah. Lew Simpson will boss the outfit and can use an 'extra.' It will be a long trip, and the crew won't get back until nearly winter. Would you like to go with Lew, Bill?"

"Oh, yes, I sure would."

"You have time to spend a few days at home," Mr. Majors added. "I'll send you word when Lew's train is ready."

Five minutes later Bill was galloping for the Cody

farm. His mother, sisters, and brother Charlie were delighted to see him again. Barking and leaping about wildly, Turk almost knocked Bill down in his joy.

The family had dozens of questions to ask about events on the trail. Bill skipped over most details about the Indian fight in order not to frighten his mother.

"Uncle Alec said you could collect my pay each month while I'm gone," he told her. "Use all of it for the things you need."

"That's wonderful of you, Billy."

"Mother! You mustn't forget that the wagon crews call me Bill now."

Mrs. Cody sighed. "I guess you'll always be Billy to me."

On his second job for Russell, Majors & Waddell, Bill had no cattle to herd. He traveled with a long train of wagons filled with supplies for soldiers serving deep in the Rocky Mountains. When he reached the distant valley of the North Platte, he would see Fort Laramie, the high plains of Wyoming, and Fort Bridger.

He rode away from Fort Leavenworth with his spirits singing. This was the life for him. He never knew anyone could be so happy as he was at that moment.

Chapter 8

CAPTURED IN THE MOUNTAINS

Bill Cody rode a mule beside Lew Simpson a mile ahead of the canvas-topped train. They paused at the crest of a long slope and glanced back at the column lurching over the rough ground.

Four yoke of oxen labored in front of each wagon loaded with six thousand pounds of freight. A bull-whacker walked beside each rig, now and then cracking his rawhide whip against the flank of a lagging steer.

It was a sight that never failed to stir Bill. Although only a week on the trail with Simpson's train, he found himself treated by all the thirty crewmen with kindness and respect. Word of his plucky fight with McCarthy's outfit had spread among the drivers. It was enough to make him a fit campmate of the rough and hardy freighters.

Indeed, Bill never thought of himself as an eleven-year-old. He lived in a world of daring and high-spirited men and he would have been offended had they treated him as anything less.

The burly Lew Simpson turned to Bill and said,

"Ride back to the herder and tell him to move his stock closer to the end wagon. He's letting them drift all over the trail. On your way, pass the word to the bullwhackers that we'll camp for the night at Willow Creek, up yonder two miles."

Bill set off with a rush, prodding his mule into a gallop. This was more play than work, and he relayed the boss's orders with a cheery voice. He could ask for nothing better than to be allowed to sit in a saddle all day.

To Fort Kearney and beyond, the train made from twelve to fifteen miles a day. As it neared Plum Creek, where the McCarthy outfit had been attacked, Bill felt a little uneasy. Would the Indians strike again to plunder and kill?

The next day, as the train skirted a row of sand hills near the North Platte, a large herd of buffaloes appeared between the river and trail. At the same time, Bill saw a group of wagons and horsemen approaching from the West on their way home from California.

Turning off the trail, the horsemen rode into the herd of buffaloes, firing rifles as they raced along. Dashing ahead of the hunters, the animals headed straight for Simpson's wagon train.

Before the bullwhackers could do anything to turn aside the stampeding mass, five hundred buffaloes were upon them. Frightened by the rush of animals, the oxen pulled around and broke for the hills. Wagon tongues snapped, chains parted, yokes were shaken off. In a moment, several wagons were overturned and freight spilled upon the ground.

Dashing out of the buffaloes' path, Bill glanced back upon a scene of mad confusion. Sweating, whip-cracking bullwhackers strained to control their terror-crazed teams. Buffaloes, oxen, and drivers were running in all directions.

A cloud of dust settled slowly upon the wreckage. The train was not only scattered but badly crippled, Bill saw. He wondered how order would ever be restored from that scene of ruin.

Although fuming over the carelessness of the hunters, Lew Simpson rode among his men giving orders for repairs. A whole day was lost shaping new wagon tongues, uprighting wagons and reloading freight. Bill was kept busy rounding up oxen and running errands for the wagon boss.

Several weeks later, the train drew near Fort Laramie, one of the most famous trading and Army posts in the West. The bullwhackers had spoken about it often, and Bill looked forward to the time when the train would camp there for a day. He might even meet some of the noted scouts and traders he had heard so much about.

He saw the whitewashed walls of Laramie when still several miles away. As he drew closer, he noticed the flats and meadows between the fort and the North Platte dotted with tepees and herds of ponies of friendly Indians. Braves, squaws, children, and dogs swarmed about the lodges.

After the wagon train made camp, Bill was free to roam about at will. He knew enough of the Indian tongue to talk with the Sioux and Cheyenne boys who readily included him in their games. He shot their bows and arrows, rode their ponies, and helped them build a raft.

The son of a Sioux chieftain named Rain-in-the-Face became especially friendly and invited Bill to the family lodge for a meal.

Inside the fort, Bill found more to interest him. He visited the soldiers' barracks, the storerooms, bakehouse, blacksmith shop, and corrals. He looked up Thomas Fitzpatrick, the Indian agent and trader, who pointed out Kit Carson, the noted mountain man, scout, and Indian fighter.

Bill gazed in awe at the small, soft-speaking Carson, the hero of many of the Wild West's boldest deeds. When, a short time later, he had a chance to meet the famous scout, Bill tingled with delight. Kit Carson stood for daring, bravery, and skill, everything the wagon train "extra" hoped some day to find in himself.

All too soon for Bill, Simpson's train was on the trail again, plodding up the rising slopes toward the

Rockies. Passing the Red Buttes, it crossed the Sweetwater and by November was moving toward Green River.

When still a day's march from that stream, the crew made its noon camp. Because the oxen had to be driven a mile and a half to water, Lew Simpson took Bill and George Woods, his assistant, to guard the animals and herders.

On the return, the group met a score of horsemen. The leader rode up to the wagon boss and said, "You're Lew Simpson, I believe."

"Right. But I don't know you."

Before the leader spoke again, the horsemen pressed closer to surround Simpson and his helpers. Bill felt a shock of fright when he saw shotguns, rifles, and revolvers leveled at him and his crewmates. His own six-shooter lay deep in its holster but he knew better than to reach for it.

"What's the meaning of this?" Simpson said crisply. "What do you want? Who are you?"

"I'm Joe Smith and my men and I are taking over your outfit. You're moving no supplies to General Johnston and his troops. Just take it easy and no one will be hurt. We'll have your shooting irons now."

Seeing that it was useless to resist, Lew sat stiffly as Joe Smith's men disarmed him and the others. Bill's heart sank when his revolver was jerked away from him.

He remembered the bullwhackers' talk in camp about a colony of people who had set up their own rule in Utah. They had drawn away from the United States government's control and warned they would fight any Army force sent against them. Now, even before Simpson's train had reached Utah, Joe Smith's men had appeared to seize the Army supplies.

As he was being led back to the corral, Bill saw that another part of Smith's force had made prisoners of the bullwhackers. Simpson turned to the enemies' leader and asked, "What's your game, Smith? What are you doing with us?"

"We're going to burn your wagons and freight so they don't reach the soldiers. The livestock we can use ourselves. We'll give you and your men enough food to reach Fort Bridger. After that you can see how you get back home."

"See here, man, you can't turn us afoot without guns," Simpson protested. "That's just plain murder."

The two leaders argued for a time and at last Smith agreed to turn over six oxen and a wagonload of food to the freight crew. Their guns were also returned to them with a warning not to pick a fight. Outnumbered by the horsemen, Simpson saw that he had to accept Smith's terms.

Ordered to set out at once, the wagon crew began to walk toward Fort Bridger, a week's march to the

West. To the surprise of Bill and his crewmates, they found Fort Bridger swarming with four hundred other employees of Russell, Majors & Waddell. Their trains, too, had been seized by armed bands from the Utah colony. A total of seventy-five wagons carrying nearly half a million pounds of freight had been destroyed. The crews had been able to save only a few oxen, horses, and mules.

The fort, built in a grove beside a trout stream, consisted of a pole stockade enclosing a log cabin, a store, and corrals. It was the trading post of James Bridger, a mountain man and scout almost as famous as Kit Carson. A tall, bearded man, he moved among the freighters with the good humor of a hotel-keeper.

Simpson left his men to talk to Bridger. When he returned his face was grave.

"We'll have to winter here with the others," he said. "Jim tells me we'll have snow before long. We can't think of starting back to Laramie until spring. We'd better get busy and build some shelters. I don't know where we'll find food enough to carry us through the winter."

Roaring storms soon covered the ground with heavy snow. Hunters found it more and more difficult to find deer and elk. Even when the men pooled their food, the meals were scant. First the oxen, then the mules and horses were butchered for meat. As the dreary weeks passed, the men were reduced to quarter rations.

Bill was always hungry and usually cold. As long as he had the strength, he walked to the mountains to carry back wood for the campfires. His respect grew for these calm men who accepted this torture as part of their life.

When winter broke at last, the arrival of a supply train for Johnston's men saved the freighters from starvation. Again able to travel, Bill and the four hundred wagonmen began the long walk to Fort Laramie. There they found plenty of food and two empty wagon trains ready to start back to Forth Leavenworth.

Taking charge of the two outfits, Lew Simpson divided the men between the trains and sent them out fifteen miles apart. Bill traveled with Simpson and Woods with the rear wagons.

Grass along the trail was scant and the livestock began to suffer. Upon reaching Ash Hollow, Simpson decided to leave the regular road and follow the North Platte River in hope of finding better pasture, even though it meant crossing a region of hostile Indians.

Mounting mules, Simpson, Bill Cody, and George Woods set out to overtake the lead train and head it for the North Platte. Each was armed with a rifle, two revolvers, and a hunting knife.

After riding seven miles, they reached a plateau back of Cedar Bluffs. Simpson scanned the hills closely and said, "Here's where we have to be careful, boys. I wouldn't be surprised——"

Before Lew finished the sentence, Bill saw a band of warriors charge out of a ravine half a mile away and race toward them.

"Lew . . . George . . . Indians!" he exclaimed. "They're coming after us."

Chapter 9

ATTACKED BY INDIANS

Even while Bill cried his warning, Simpson and Woods began to whip their mules into a gallop. Bill found himself trailing the others in the dash to escape.

Hardly a minute passed before he saw that the Indians' speedy ponies would soon overtake the slower mules. There were at least fifty warriors in the band. The distance between them and the three whites closed rapidly. Escape was impossible, Bill saw.

Simpson, holding his glance upon the Indians, suddenly called out, "Stop, boys. Jump off your mules."

Bill obeyed without thinking. He had no idea of what Lew planned to do; he was too alarmed to reason for himself.

In astonishment, he saw Simpson draw a revolver and shoot all three mules. As the animals dropped, the wagon boss said, "Grab hold, boys. Drag them close together . . . we'll make a fort out of them . . . give us some protection. Hurry!"

In less than a minute, they had the mules pulled around to form a triangle. They leaped inside the barrier and leveled rifles across the bodies just as the Indians swept down upon them, howling fiercely.

Their rifles cracked together. Three braves toppled from their ponies. The others turned aside after firing a shower of arrows that tore into the dead mules.

The warriors charged once more. They again lost three of their number as the whites' rifles roared, but this time they drove in closer as though bent upon overrunning the tiny fort.

A blast of revolver fire caught them by surprise. They wavered and broke, pulling out of range. As Bill reloaded his guns, he saw the redmen begin to circle the barrier. Clinging to the sides of their mounts, they shot from under the ponies' necks.

"Only two of them have rifles," Bill heard Simpson say. "They'll think twice before getting too close to us again."

"Lew, jerk this arrow out of my shoulder," Woods said. Bill glanced around. For the first time he noticed that George had been hit. As he watched, the wagon boss took a firm hold of the shaft and pulled it free. Woods gritted his teeth but made no sound.

After glancing at the arrow tip, Simpson said, "It's not poisoned, George. Good thing. Here, let me patch up the hole."

By the time Lew had applied a wad of tobacco, the Indians had gathered for a council of war well out

"Jerk this arrow out of my shoulder," cried Woods

of rifle range. Simpson said, "Here's our chance to build up our fort. Get out your knives, boys, and throw up some dirt. It'll give us more room to wiggle around in."

When the warriors ended their meeting, they began a new type of attack. Several lighted torches and with them set fire to the grass. Driven by the

84

wind, the flames spread toward the crowded refuge of the three whites.

As the smoke drifted over him, Bill's eyes began to smart. He strained to see through the haze and noticed mounted warriors moving up behind it.

"Look out, they're coming again," he warned, as he fired at the advancing braves. Simpson and Woods joined in driving back the attackers.

Bill noticed with relief that the grass was too short to make a strong fire. When the flames began to flicker out, the Indians again took up their circling attack.

The siege dragged on through the afternoon. Now and then a warrior dashed close for a quick shot, but even these thrusts stopped after the whites picked off the more daring riders.

At dusk the Indians formed a wide circle around the little fort. They slid from their ponies, drew blankets around themselves and settled down for the night.

"They're playing a waiting game," Simpson said. "Maybe they figure to starve us out. Anyway, they're going to see that we don't sneak away during the dark."

"I was hoping our wagon train would catch up with us before this," Bill said. "But it's in camp now." Trying to be more cheerful, he added, "It'll reach us in the morning."

"We have to hold out until then," Simpson said. "What worries me—those redskins may move in on us in the dark. Keep your eyes peeled."

The long hours of waiting began. Hunger and thirst became a grinding pain. Bill knew Lew and George suffered as much as he did, but neither had a word of complaint. His cramped position between the mules made him stiff and sore. Every move increased the ache in his muscles. Cold and dampness added to their misery.

By midnight Bill had to fight to keep his eyes open. George Woods had not moved for a long time and Bill felt sure he was asleep. Lew Simpson had settled back against a dead mule with his feet braced against the one opposite him.

With a start, Bill saw a blurred form creep silently toward him. Two others followed, the faintest of shadows.

He reached out and touched Lew's arm. "They're sneaking up on us," he whispered. "Out there, over to the left——"

Simpson was alert in an instant. He peered in the direction Bill pointed and slowly brought up his rifle. He waited a long minute and then the blast from his gun broke the night's silence. George Woods snapped out of his sleep.

A groan sounded from the darkness and then the heavy calm settled over the plain again.

"I guess that one won't bother us any more," Lew said. He patted Bill's shoulder. "Good boy, Bill. You've got an eagle eye." He paused a minute before adding, "You've been a real scrapper in this fight, Bill. Just keep your nerve and we'll get out of this."

As dawn spread across the battleground, Bill took new hope. The Indians were still huddled in their wide circle, evidently planning to let time work for them against the stubborn whites.

Bill's patience wore thin as the morning advanced. He strained his ears for any sound that would tell him the wagon train was coming to their rescue. He squirmed to his knees when a distant crack—the pop of a bullwhacker's whip—cut through the morning air.

"They're coming, Lew . . . George!" he almost shouted. "The wagons are coming."

A slow smile crossed Simpson's face. "That's powerful sweet music to me," he said. He sobered quickly. "The redskins have heard it, too. Get ready, boys. They'll be on us in a minute."

The warriors had drawn into formation for another charge. With angry howls, they bore down upon the three whites in a last furious assault.

Firing until rifles and revolvers were empty, the trio again beat off the braves. The attackers left dozens of their arrows sticking in the bodies of the mules.

When a party of horsemen from the wagon train galloped over a rise in the plain, the braves raced away in defeat. Bill was on his feet cheering madly when the rescuers reached him and his companions.

A worried but happy family greeted Bill on his return. He was surprised to find that his mother had opened a small hotel in Salt Creek valley. His wages, which she had collected during his absence, had helped to start the new business.

"Gracous, Billy . . . Bill, how you've grown," Mrs. Cody said upon seeing him. "And you're nicer looking than ever."

"I'm twelve now, Mother. I had a birthday when I was at Fort Bridger."

"You must have had a terrible winter in the mountains. Did the Indians trouble you? I'm sure you ran from them, as we told you to."

"Well, you can't always run from Indians, Mother. Sometimes you have to chase them away."

Mrs. Cody shuddered. Then a warm light filled her eyes and she said, "You have been such a great help to us, Bill. Between your wages and the hotel, we're getting on nicely."

Bill spent a month with his family. By late spring, he started west again with a wagon train bound for Fort Laramie, this time as a bullwhacker. During the summer he worked around Laramie, where he again met Kit Carson, Jim Bridger, and other scouts and guides whose tales of adventure stirred him deeply.

Bill also became friendly with the fur trappers who sold their pelts to the post trader. Eager to increase his earnings, he quit his job with Russell, Majors & Waddell that fall and set out with two trappers to work the streams north of the fort.

The venture failed; Bill barely caught enough furs to pay for his food. Selling his traps, he returned home in February in time to observe his thirteenth birthday with his family.

At his mother's urging, Bill now went back to school. He realized the weakness of his education, and for two and a half months he studied hard to improve his reading and writing. It was the longest period of schooling in his life.

In that year of 1859, the discovery of gold near Pikes Peak brought a rush of fortune hunters into the West. The trail past the Cody hotel became crowded with wagon trains, horsemen, and even some pulling handcarts or pushing wheelbarrows, all bound for the gold field. A new stagecoach line from Fort Leavenworth to Denver sped the more well-to-do gold hunters to Colorado.

Naturally, Bill Cody caught the gold fever, too. With two young friends, he made plans to join the westward parade. Mrs. Cody tried to discourage Bill, but he would not be denied this chance to strike it rich.

He provided a farm wagon while his companions furnished the mules. With what money they could scrape together, they bought beans, bacon, coffee, flour, gold pans, picks, and shovels.

In high spirits, the trio set out on the seven-hundred-mile march, walking every step of the way. Like the others, their slogan was, "Pikes Peak or Bust."

Chapter 10

THE WARRIORS' VISIT

Reaching Denver in the early summer, Bill and his companions found it a wild and crowded city. Nearby Cherry Creek had given up all its gold to the early-comers; the others were forced to look in more distant places.

Like most of the fortune seekers, Bill and his pals knew nothing about gold mining. Moving on to Golden and Black Hawk, they panned the gravel that others had probably worked before them. In two months they were broke.

Hundreds of miners were in the same pinch. The golden bubble had burst, and there was nothing to do but return home. Bill traded the wagon and mules for food to give him and his friends supplies for the journey.

In no mood to walk the seven hundred miles, Bill thought of another means. Why not build a raft and float down the Platte and Missouri rivers all the way to Fort Leavenworth? His companions welcomed the plan and after lashing several logs together, the three set out.

All went well until they were within a mile of Julesburg, Colorado. There the swift current wrecked the raft, dumping riders, gear, and food into the stream. Bill and his companions swam to safety, saving only the clothes they wore.

At Julesburg, Bill went to the Russell, Majors & Waddell freight corrals and found a friend, George Chrisman, in charge of the station. He had no trouble winning Chrisman's consent to let him and his pals ride back to Leavenworth with an empty wagon train.

Although he said little about it, Bill smarted over his failure as a gold hunter. For a year he had given little to his family's support. He wanted to earn money, quickly if possible, to make up for this lack.

His thoughts turned again and again to the bales of furs he had seen at Fort Laramie. Furs were valuable and could be turned into money quickly. Despite his first lack of success at it, he believed trapping offered the best hope of earning a year's wages in a few months.

Bill decided David Harrington, a friend a few years older than he, could be interested in making a fur hunt. Dave did not disappoint him. They agreed to work the creeks leading into the Republican River of western Kansas.

Loading a wagon with traps, food, tools, and ammunition they set out in the late fall of 1859. At

Mrs. Cody's suggestion, Bill added his schoolbooks to the camp gear. There would be long winter evenings when he could work at his reading.

Using the skill learned from Kit Carson, Jim Bridger, and other mountain men, Bill scouted the streams until he found a region swarming with beaver and game. It was deep in the wilderness, one hundred and twenty-five miles from the closest settler. Although they had sighted no Indians, Bill and Dave were always on the alert.

A room-sized hollow in a creek bank became the young trappers' winter camp. They put up a log wall across the front, made a stone fireplace beside the doorway and laid poles on the floor to keep it dry. After building bunks and closing the wall chinks with mud, they had a snug hut.

Their two oxen were allowed to graze during the day, but at night they were penned in a pole corral near the dugout.

In the first few weeks, Bill and Dave had to work into the night to skin the beaver they trapped. To his delight, Bill watched the pile of furs grow. The winter's catch would exceed his best hopes, he saw.

The two trappers were startled one night to hear the oxen bellow and race around in their corral. Grabbing rifles, Bill and Dave dashed from the cabin.

A dark form reared before them as they reached the pen. With an angry roar, the animal lunged at

Dave. Bill raised his rifle and fired into the monster's gaping mouth. The beast fell dead in front of Dave, and only then did Bill see that it was a large black bear.

"Wow!" Dave gasped. "That was a close one for me, Bill. I was too scared——"

Bill hurried past the slain animal to examine one of the oxen stretched out on the corral floor. The other one paced about nervously.

"Dave, get a lantern, quick," Bill said. "I'm afraid one of our steers has been crippled."

When Dave had returned with the light, Bill saw that the bear had clawed the ox so badly it had to be killed. Although this act raised a serious problem—how to move the wagon with its furs in the spring—there was no answer for it at the moment.

"We'll have to get another ox later," Bill said. "We'll think of a way when the time comes."

Not long after the bear's raid, the trappers were hunting elk near their camp when Bill slipped and broke his leg just above the ankle. Helped by Dave, he hobbled back to the dugout and fell groaning upon his bunk. As best he could, Dave fastened splints over the break and tried to ease his companion's pain.

"Now we are in for it, Dave," Bill sighed. "I'm as helpless as a papoose."

"There's only one thing for me to do," Dave said.

94

"Go after a team of oxen so that I can haul you back home. I'll ride on the steer we still have."

"It's a long trip to the nearest settler," said Bill. "More than a hundred miles."

"I hate to leave you here alone, Bill, but there's no other way. I should be back in about twenty days. I'll take enough furs to pay for what we need."

Dave brought in a large heap of wood, filled buckets and pans with water and cooked up a supply of food. Then he made a pair of crude crutches for Bill.

"By the time you run low on food, you'll be able to hobble around and cook more," Dave said.

Bill hated to see his companion go but made no protest. He tried to be cheerful when Dave left, but it was a weak effort.

Unused to idleness and being alone, Bill found the days endless. He read his books, slept as much as he could and practiced walking on his crutches. He kept track of time by notching a stick to mark each dreary, dragging day.

By the end of two weeks, he was able to move about the cabin fairly well. He tried to picture Dave bursting into the cabin, and yet he knew another week must pass before that was possible.

Bill had fallen asleep over a book when he was startled by a hand upon his shoulder. He looked up into the painted face of a Sioux Indian.

Hiding his fright, he said, "How." He noticed six other warriors had crowded into the dugout and heard more outside. To his vast relief, he recognized their leader as Rain-in-the-Face, a chieftain he had met at Fort Laramie. Quickly he reminded the Indian of their friendship.

"Why you here?" Rain-in-the-Face asked.

Bill pointed to his bandaged leg and explained how he had broken it. While he talked, the braves pressed about him with raised knives and tomahawks. Their leader held them back.

"Braves hunt scalps," said Rain-in-the-Face. He paused to let Bill think about that. Finally he added, "Paleface my friend. No take him scalp. Need food."

Again the chieftain had to order the braves away from Bill. They obeyed but grumbled angrily. Bill's supply of food caught their attention and they grunted happily as they set about cooking a feast for themselves.

Their meal finished, the warriors gathered up Bill's rifles, revolver and ammunition. The young trapper's heart sank as his unwelcome guests bundled up the remaining sugar, coffee, flour and salt. He almost cried out in protest but held his tongue.

At the last moment, Rain-in-the-Face left a small amount of flour and meat with Bill. It was enough to last him a week if he stretched it to the limit.

Although glad to see the last of the Indians, Bill had

Bill's unwelcome guests bundled up the remaining food supplies

another worry to plague him. Suppose they met Dave? Perhaps Dave would never reach him now. Then what would happen to him?

A few days after the Indians' visit, a blizzard struck the Republican River valley. The wind howled hour after hour, piling snow around the dugout.

Where was Dave? Bill wondered. Had he become lost in the storm? Perhaps he couldn't find the cabin. He might have frozen to death.

As the days passed with maddening slowness and Dave was still absent, the strain was almost more than Bill could bear. He could not read or sleep. His taste for food left him. Only a few sticks of firewood remained.

He counted the notches that marked the passing time. Twenty-seven days. One more and Dave would have been gone four weeks. Somehow Bill worried through another night.

The next day began the same as the others. He went to the door time after time to gaze out upon a white desert unbroken by a single trail. At last he threw himself upon his bunk and fell asleep out of sheer weakness.

He awoke suddenly as though alarmed by a bad dream. Every sense was alert. What was that? A cry? A shout?

Faintly it came again. "Bill. Oh, Bill."

He jumped up so quickly he sent his crutches flying. Crawling across the floor for them, he fairly bounded to the door and pulled it open.

No one was in sight. The sun shining upon the snow dazzled him. Maybe he was losing his mind and was imagining things, Bill told himself.

Then the cry came again. "I'm coming, Bill."

98

"D-Dave!" Bill's mouth went dry, and he couldn't utter another sound. Now he could see Dave, urging a team of oxen toward the dugout. Each animal carried a pack of supplies.

In a short time, Dave was inside the cabin with Bill. Their greeting filled the room with a happy din, and many minutes passed before they could control their joy even to start a meal.

They talked for hours about the trials they had faced and overcome. Dave explained that he had reached the settler without trouble and started back with a new team of oxen. Then the blizzard had overtaken him and he found shelter in a canyon, where he was forced to remain two days. After that the deep snow had slowed his travel.

As soon as Dave could load the wagon with their furs, traps, and camp gear, the trappers started for home. To his disgust, Bill was forced to ride during the whole journey because of his injury.

They reached Fort Leavenworth in March of 1860, sold their pelts for a high price and divided the profits. Despite his accident, Bill had a good sum to turn over to his mother.

At Leavenworth, Bill heard news of a daring project planned by Russell, Majors & Waddell that made him forget about fur trapping and wagon trains. The freight company, in answer to demands of California miners and settlers, was about to start a fast mail and express service across the West.

Mounted on swift horses, relays of riders would race two thousand miles between St. Joseph, Missouri, and Sacramento in ten days, fifteen days faster than the stagecoaches. The new mail line would be known as the "pony express."

Here was something made to order for Bill Cody's love of excitement and adventure. Along the dangerous plains and mountain trail, the riders would have to deal alone with Indians, outlaws, storms, snow, and flooded rivers. For risking their lives in this manner, they would be paid one hundred and twenty-five dollars a month.

The best Bill could hope for as a bullwhacker was forty dollars. The high pay of the pony express became his goal.

But his broken leg was still far from healed. He spent the weeks after his return home building up his strength to become an expressman. When he could again ride with his usual dash and daring, he set out to ask for the job.

Chapter 11

PONY EXPRESS RIDER

George Chrisman looked at Bill Cody again, his eyes sweeping the tall, wiry body clad in fringed buckskin. Then his eyes met the piercing stare that pleaded with him silently.

"Sure, Bill, you look older than your fourteen years," Chrisman said at last. "But that doesn't make you old enough."

"You're hiring young riders for the express," Bill pointed out. "I don't see why you can't take me."

"Now if you were about twenty, even eighteen. . . . Our boys have to be real lightweights."

"I don't weigh more than a hundred and twenty. I'm a good rider, George. And I know how to handle a gun. Any kind of gun."

Chrisman nodded. "Sure, Bill, that you do. But the trail out here is really rugged. I'm not saying you couldn't handle it." The boss of the Julesburg division of the express thought for a minute. "Why don't you see Bill Trotter? He's bossing a stretch at the eastern end of the line. You're more apt to get a job from Bill. It wouldn't hurt to ask."

Bill saw it was useless to argue longer with George. He wanted a job carrying the express, and even if it had to be across a stretch of plain as safe and easy as a rocking chair, he'd take it. But later he'd ask to be sent farther west, where he could expect a little excitement.

Even Bill Trotter wasn't too eager to make a place for Bill Cody. He agreed finally to give him a month's trial, and Bill became the youngest of the eighty riders who sped with the mail to California and back.

The two-thousand-mile trail had been divided into sections, forty-five to eighty-five miles long, over which a rider raced. Relay stations, where fresh mounts were held for the riders, were set up about fifteen miles apart.

Station keepers lived at the relay points to care for the four hundred ponies needed for the service. On the longer runs, the riders changed horses half a dozen times.

These mounts were California mustangs, tough and swift animals that could outrun the fastest Indian ponies. The riders were armed with revolvers and hunting knives but were ordered not to stop and fight unless cornered. They were to depend upon the speed of their mounts to carry them out of trouble.

At the starting points—St. Joseph and Sacramento —the mail was locked into four pouches set into the corners of a leather apron called a "mochila." This leather square fitted over the small saddle so that a rider sat upon it when mounted. At each relay point, the mochila was quickly stripped from one horse and slapped upon the back of the waiting mount. Two minutes were allowed a rider for this exchange, but some were able to make the swing in thirty seconds.

Because speed was all-important, the riders' load of mail weighed twenty pounds or less. Letters were usually written on tissue paper, since the express charges were five dollars for half an ounce. The mail was wrapped in oiled silk before being placed in the pouches to keep it dry.

Started on April 3, 1860, the pony express was an immediate success. Riding day and night, the carriers passed along their mochilas without delay, the last rider delivering the mail ten days after it had started its long journey.

The fast time surprised and thrilled the nation. The express riders became new heroes in the struggle to conquer the West.

Bill Cody took little pride in his part, although he never failed to finish his run on time. The only breaks in his unexciting three-hour ride came at the three relay stations on his route. He longed for the time when he could ride for George Chrisman or Alf Slade, out where Indians and outlaws offered a challenge.

His month's trial went on for another thirty days.

Then he received a message that ended it for a time. His mother, never strong, had become ill again, and Bill was needed at home. Grudgingly, he turned in his saddle and mochila to help run Mrs. Cody's hotel.

Bill had hardly returned home before the Pah-Ute Indians started a war in Nevada that shut down the pony express for nearly six weeks. Attacking relay points in the mountains and across the desert, they killed station keepers, burned the buildings, and ran off valuable express horses. Troops had to move into the Far West to put down the uprising.

Although Russell, Majors & Waddell suffered losses of seventy-five thousand dollars in the raids, they rebuilt the stations, bought more ponies, and hired new station men. By midsummer the express riders were again pounding over the trail.

Mrs. Cody's health improved during the weeks Bill was home. When he saw that he could be spared, Bill hired a man to help his mother and rode to Fort Leavenworth to call on Alec Majors.

"I'm ready to ride the express again, Uncle Alec. But this time I want to go farther west."

Mr. Majors nodded. "We're having a hard time keeping good riders beyond Laramie, Bill. Indians and road agents are too much for some of the boys and they're quitting. I'll give you a letter to Alf Slade, out at the Horseshoe station."

"Thank you, Uncle Alec. I'm ready to go."

Bill worked his way to Fort Laramie as a bull-whacker with one of Lew Simpson's freight trains and then rode to where Alf Slade, a tough but trusted division boss, had his quarters.

At first, Slade brushed Bill aside with the remark, "I don't hire kids for my run. Go away, you bother me."

"But Mr. Slade, I rode for Bill Trotter and Mr. Majors thinks I'll do. He says so in this letter."

"So you rode for Bill Trotter?" Slade said in surprise. "Well now, that's different. All right, I'll give you a chance, because I sure can use some boys with guts. If you can carry the mail on my division, you can go anywhere."

Bill quickly learned that he had taken on a man-sized chore. His seventy-six-mile run, from Red Buttes on the North Platte to Three Crossings on the Sweetwater River, cut through rough and broken country. He changed horses five times, but even so they ended their relays worn out.

At the western end of his run, he rode up a canyon through which a river boiled from wall to wall. In a distance of a few rods, he splashed across the stream three times. Indians or outlaws were likely to lurk in any one of a dozen places.

A short time after starting to work for Slade, Bill had a taste of what to expect. Upon finishing his run to Three Crossings, he was told by the station keeper that the rider supposed to relieve him had been killed in a fight the night before.

"You'll have to carry through to Rocky Ridge, Bill," the keeper said. "There's no other rider here to go."

"How far is Rocky Ridge?"

"Eighty-five miles."

Bill bit his lip. He thought of the hot meal and rest his body craved. Then he remembered Alf Slade's challenge and said, "All right. Get me some bread and meat so I can eat while I ride. Let's not waste any time."

Six hours later, Bill rode into the Rocky Ridge station. He had barely reached it before the rider from the West galloped in. Although stiff and sore, Bill swung the mail bags upon his saddle, mounted and started for the East, over the long trail he had just covered.

On and on he rode, through Three Crossings and to his home station at Red Buttes. Nearly dead from weariness, he delivered the mail on time, having traveled three hundred and twenty-two miles in twenty-one hours. He tired out twenty horses on his run, one of the longest in the history of the pony express.

Jack Keetley, another express rider, once rode more than three hundred miles without rest, having covered the last part of his run asleep in the saddle.

Pony Bob Haslam chalked up a record ride of

three hundred and eighty miles as an express carrier. He had eleven hours' rest between the start and finish, however.

In 1861, the bitterness between North and South over slavery broke into civil war. The pony express riders sped the news to California but to them, and to fifteen-year-old Bill Cody, the war was distant and unreal.

The people of the West had their own troubles to worry over. With the Army giving most of its attention to the fighting in the South, the western bullwhackers, stagecoach drivers, and pony expressmen were left largely to their own efforts to meet attacks of hostile Indians.

The Indians became especially troublesome along the Sweetwater that year, and Bill saw more than enough of them. Although alert for any hint of danger, he was ambushed one day by fifteen braves when eight miles from Horse Creek. Pressing himself flat upon his pony's back, he outsped the pack.

Arriving at the station, he was dismayed to find that the warriors had paid an earlier call. They had killed the stock tender, burned the buildings, and stolen the spare horses. Bill was forced to ride his fagged-out mount another twelve miles to the Ploutz station before getting a fresh pony.

Not long after this scare, Bill received a station keeper's warning of many Indian signs on the trail ahead. The express route lay through a wild section, marked by a deep valley that narrowed sharply at its outlet. About halfway through the valley, a boulder stood in the open.

Although feeling sure that he would meet the warriors there if anywhere, Bill galloped into the valley. A high cliff stood on one side and timber covered a steep slope on the other.

From a distance, he saw a spot of color beside the huge rock. It disappeared at once, before he could be sure it was a feather from a brave's headdress.

Riding on boldly, Bill kept to the trail until within gun range of the boulder. Swerving sharply, he swung himself to his pony's side and angled away from the rock just as a rifle shot sounded from behind it. The bullet whistled over Bill's back.

As though the shot were a signal, a score of mounted Indians broke from the timber and sped to cut off Bill. Spurring his horse, Bill raced to beat them to the narrow end of the valley.

Drawing his revolver, he glanced across at the whooping warriors. Their chieftain rode a swift pony and was soon ahead of the pack. Bill saw that the leader was the one he must fear most.

Their mounts pounding along at top speed, Bill and the chieftain drew toward the valley's narrow pass. When only thirty yards apart, the riders raised their weapons, the Indian stretching his bow, Bill

108

leveling his revolver, each aiming with deadly intent.

Arrow and bullet darted at their targets. Bill saw the chieftain flinch as the lead caught him. With a cry of pain, he toppled from his mount.

A chorus of angry shouts, followed by a rain of arrows, reached out after Bill. A moment later, the young express rider dashed into the choked pass and galloped out of the valley. The braves chased him to within sight of the next relay station, but by then he was far in the lead. When he dismounted, he found an arrow sticking into his horse's flank.

Wagon trains and stagecoaches were only a little more safe than the express riders from Indian attack. So many horses were run off from relay stations that the riders and drivers were having trouble moving mail and passengers.

Then a war party attacked a stagecoach between Split Rock and Three Crossings and killed the driver and two passengers.

A group of outraged trail workers met at Red Buttes to plan a way to punish the Indians. When a tall, bronzed man, whose hair hung to his shoulders, spoke to the crowd, all listened with respect. He was looked upon as the leader.

Although it was the first time he had seen the man, Bill Cody did not have to be told that this was James Butler Hickok, known to his friends as Wild Bill. Hickok, then a stagecoach driver, had already proved himself one of the West's fastest men on the draw.

Bill could not take his eyes off Wild Bill. His quiet manners, his soft voice, the long hair, and two pearl-handled revolvers at his side made a deep impression. Bill was surprised to find that Hickok was only twenty-four—barely nine years older than himself. He promised himself that some day he would pattern his looks after his new hero.

"We want about forty men for this job," Bill heard Hickok say. "It'll take some hard riding and maybe a bit of powder burning. We'll teach the red-skins a lesson if we get a chance, but most of all, we want to get back those horses. Now, how many of you think you're cut out for it?"

A score spoke up quickly, then others volunteered. Bill moved up and said, "Mr. Hickok, I'd like to go with you."

Wild Bill looked at the young express carrier sternly. He measured him for a minute before saying, "You're Bill Cody, aren't you?"

Surprised that the man knew him, Bill stammered a reply.

"You'll do, Bill," Hickok said. "I've heard about your work with Lew Simpson and your riding with the express. You're the kind of fellow I want."

The party was soon made up and preparations finished for the start. Early the next morning, the forty horsemen set out toward the Powder River.

Chapter 12

BILL FIGHTS OUTLAWS

Although the youngest among the forty men starting the Indian hunt, Bill Cody was the most carefree. After the hard riding required of an expressman, this jaunt was a vacation. He enjoyed the company of old and new friends, but most of all he was excited by this chance to ride with Wild Bill Hickok. Whenever he could, he pushed himself to the leader's side.

In the next few days, the Indian trail led north from the Platte, then west toward the Big Horn mountains to the Crazy Woman fork. Here it became clear that other bands of warriors had joined the first, bringing more stolen horses.

Wild Bill halted to confer with his riders. "We're getting close to the main bunch," he said, "and from now on we have to look alive. While I ride ahead to scout the trail, the rest of you take it easy. Keep off the ridges."

More cautiously, the men moved behind Wild Bill toward Clear Creek, another branch of the Powder River. Bill Cody felt the tension among his companions. They were now deep in Sioux country where whites rarely ventured without Army escort.

Presently Wild Bill galloped back to halt his men. "There's a big camp with a lot of hosses on the far bank of the creek, three miles yonder," he said. "There're too many redskins for us to handle in a standup fight. We'll lay low back here until dark and then make a surprise visit. Our only chance is to stampede the stock."

Several hours of daylight remained before the group could attack. Hickok forbade the lighting of campfires, and most of the men napped until dark. Bill Cody was too excited to think of sleep.

Night settled upon the hills at last, and the leader gave the word to advance. Bill rode near the head of the group, eager to be among the first to fall upon the warriors. He had some scores to settle with them.

The whites approached the creek unnoticed. At a signal from Hickok, the riders charged upon the camp, shouting wildly and firing rifles and revolvers.

The surprise attack stunned the Indians. They dashed about in confusion as the horsemen swept over them. From the camp, the raiders sped to a nearby flat where scores of horses grazed. The entire herd broke before the surge of horsemen and in a moment was in wild stampede.

Turning the mounts across the creek, the whites headed them south, driving them for several miles before halting to rest. They had not only recovered all of their stolen horses but had taken at least a hundred Indian ponies.

Elated by their success, half the riders turned back to complete their rout of the warriors. Without mounts, the Indians were forced to scatter into the hills to save their lives.

Four days later, the Hickok party reached the Sweetwater station with their horses. The stagecoaches rolled again, and Bill Cody returned to his express run, free for a time from attack.

But the trail was never without its danger for the riders. More and more often, large sums of money were being sent by express, and outlaws had made several attempts to hold up and rob the carriers.

One day Alf Slade came to Bill with a report that he would have to carry several thousand dollars on his next trip.

"I know, Mr. Slade," Bill said. "I was told about it at Red Buttes. I guess everybody along the line knows it now."

"You can just figure that the road agents heard about it, too," Slade said. "They may make a play for it on our division. There are plenty of spots where they can ambush a rider."

Bill became thoughtful. At last he said, "I think I can outsmart them, Mr. Slade. I have an idea."

"I hope it's a good one," Slade said.

Bill had time enough to work out his scheme before the rider from the East reached him. Taking a spare mochila, he stuffed the front pouches with paper to make them appear filled with money. Then he folded a blanket to fit snugly under his saddle. He was ready when the rider he was to relieve dashed into the station.

Hurriedly stripping the mail pouches from the sweating horse, Bill placed them upon his own mount. Over them he spread the blanket so that it hid the mochila with the bank notes. Next he cinched his saddle in place and upon that fitted the pouches stuffed with paper.

A moment later he was off, galloping into the hills to the West. Even though looking for a gunman in every clump of trees or rock-strewn gully along the trail, he was startled when a bearded outlaw stepped into his path from a thicket in a narrow ravine.

At once another road agent sprang up, a few yards behind the first. Both leveled rifles at the rider. Bill skidded his horse to a stop.

"Hands up, boy!" the first robber called. "Give us the money. Hand it over peaceful-like and you won't get hurt."

"You're stopping the government mail," Bill said, trying to hold his voice steady. "Let me by, if you know what's good for you."

"All we want is the money, boy," the outlaw said.

A bearded outlaw watched Bill from behind a boulder

His voice hardened. "Give it to us pronto or this will be your last ride. We're not fooling around with you."

"You'll hang for this——"

The first outlaw aimed his rifle at Bill's head. "Are you tossing the money bags to me or do I have to——"

Bill took courage in a show of anger. "Well, all right. But you'll hang——"

He tugged at the mochila under him and pulled it free. "Here, take it," he said, and flung it at the nearest robber's head.

The man ducked and turned to pick up the bags. Bill dropped his hand to his holster, jerked out the revolver, and fired at the second robber, striking him in the arm.

At the same moment, Bill spurred his horse into a sudden leap. Its foreleg struck the man still crouched over and fumbling for the mailbags. Sent sprawling, the robber lost hold of his rifle and before he could recover it, Bill was galloping up the trail, the money safe under him.

A rifle shot sounded behind him and a bullet whined past his shoulder. Bill pressed himself to his horse's back and sped out of range of the outlaws' fire. He finished his run unharmed and passed on his mail pouches intact.

Unaware of it himself, Bill began to show by the spring of 1861 the strain of the long, hard hours in the saddle. He lost weight and slept poorly. The change in his daring young rider did not escape Alf Slade.

"I'm taking you off the run for a spell, Bill," the division boss said. "You're worn out and need a rest."

"I'm all right, Mr. Slade," Bill protested. "I don't need——"

"Yes you do, Bill," Slade said firmly. "I want you

to help look after the stock at the station and be handy when I need a relief rider. But for a few days, just take it easy. Do a little hunting and fishing."

As he thought about it, Bill realized that his early zest for carrying the mail had weakened. He was not alone in that feeling. Few riders could endure the long hours of pounding over the trail, and changes among them were frequent.

Bill enjoyed to the utmost his free time to roam over the hills and canyons around the express station. When he did relieve a rider now and then, it was a welcome break in his idleness.

Promising to bring in some fresh game for supper, Bill started his hunt one day on a scrawny horse owned by the station keeper. On the lookout for sagehens, he rode farther than he intended to, but finally shot a pair.

As he turned toward home late in the day, he entered a wooded ravine in which he noted many hoof marks. Puzzling over this evidence of horses in that remote region, he rode on until eight riders rounded a bend in the trail. They were upon him before he could even think of hiding.

From their hard looks and fierce appearance, Bill knew at once that this was an outlaw band, either road agents or horse thieves. With a start, he recognized two of them as former teamsters with one of Lew Simpson's wagon trains.

"Howdy, gents," he said.

"What are you doing around here, punk?" the leader growled.

"Hunting." Bill held up his two sagehens. "I'm heading for the Horseshoe station. Got anything against that?"

One of Simpson's former bullwhackers spoke up. "That's Bill Cody, boss. He carries mail for Slade."

"One of Alf Slade's boys, eh?" the leader said. "I guess we'd better——" He turned to Bill. "Come along to camp with us, Cody. Maybe you'd like to have a bite with us."

Bill felt the evil intent behind the invitation, and he knew better than to resist. "Sure, boss," he said. "Glad to."

Bill waited until the horsemen started up before turning his mount to join them. One hung back, however, and said, "Move ahead, Cody. I'll stay back here so you won't get lost." He laughed at his clever joke.

Riding at an easy lope, the group did not slow down until it swung into a canyon thick with brush and saplings.

Bill thought, "I have to do something before we get to their hideout." He noted that the riders were now strung out in single file, the leader fifty yards ahead of him. Darkness was settling; the gloom was already thick in the canyon.

Bill let one of the sagehens slip from his fingers. "Oops!" he exclaimed. Stopping his horse, he glanced at the rider behind. "Will you pick up that hen for me, Cap?"

"Clumsy ox," the horseman muttered, but he stepped down and leaned over to reach the hen. Bill was upon him instantly, cracking him across the skull with his revolver butt. With a groan, the man hit the ground.

The sound of the blow carried to the rider in front of Bill. His hand was upon his six-shooter when Bill swung about to face him. Before he could raise it, Bill fired and the man fell from his saddle.

Spurring his horse, Bill raced down the trail. The curses and the beat of hoofs told him that the others were following. Crouching low, he urged his mount to speed up.

It was useless, Bill realized then. The plug he rode was no express pony and no match either for the pursuing horsemen.

Rounding a bend in the trail, Bill leaped from his mount, giving him a hearty slap as he did so. Throwing himself into a clump of brush, he hid until six outlaws thundered past after the riderless horse.

Scrambling up the ravine's steep slope, Bill climbed until he was breathless. No horse could follow him there, he was sure. But he must have the ridge between him and the gang before he could feel safe.

At daylight he stumbled footsore, hungry, and scratched into the Horseshoe station. Another rider carried word to Slade of Bill's brush with the outlaws. The division boss rounded up twenty men to ride against the outlaw band. With Bill guiding them, they found the hideout, but it was deserted and the thieves had escaped.

As had happened before, a letter from home called Bill back to Kansas. Mrs. Cody was again seriously ill and wanted her son near.

It was not a matter of money now. Bill had been earning good wages, most of which he sent to his mother. He was torn between her appeal and his loyalty to the pony express.

When Bill showed the letter to Alf Slade, the division boss urged him to go at once. "You've been a good man, Bill, but it's only a question of time before the express would be too much for you. A fellow can take just so much of it."

Bill rode to Fort Laramie and from there worked his way home with a wagon train. He found conditions far different from the way he had left them.

Chapter 13

WAR AND MARRIAGE

While out in the Wyoming mountains fighting Indians and outlaws, Bill thought of the Civil War, when he thought of it at all, as a conflict in another world. Upon his return home, he found it very real indeed.

Along the Missouri River, the war had become a cruel and bloody struggle. Kansas was a free state and Missouri was slave. The fiery and hot-headed citizens of both were at each other's throats almost daily.

The memory of how his father had been hounded to his death was sharp in Bill's mind. It was not in his nature to keep out of a fight where he might pay off an old score. Joining groups of horsemen in hit-and-run raids upon Missouri enemies, he became a daring Jayhawker in the border clashes.

When Mrs. Cody learned what Bill was up to, she made him stop. That kind of behavior was wicked and lawless, she said, and no fit business for a fifteen-year-old. Bill stayed home until his unrest forced him into some new venture.

When he saw that his mother's health was better,

he thought of returning to the pony express. But by the summer of 1861, the end of the fast mail service was in sight. A telegraph line, stretching from Missouri to the Pacific coast, would be finished in October. When the last pole was set and the wires joined, telegrams could be sent across the United States in seconds. The need for the pony express would then be over.

Bill never thought of a job unless horses had a part in it. As long as he could ride, he was contented. His skill as a horseman made him known to everyone along the western trails.

Going to Fort Leavenworth, he had no trouble finding work with the Army. All dispatches between Army posts were carried by riders on fast horses. For the rest of the summer and fall, Bill ran messages between Leavenworth and Fort Larned, Kansas, well out on the Santa Fe Trail.

That winter he helped a friend, George Long, buy cavalry horses for the Army from stock growers and farmers in Missouri and Kansas. He was home now and then but never longer than a few days.

Spring brought a rash of Indian raids upon wagon trains and settlers west of Fort Leavenworth. A volunteer regiment of soldiers was raised in Kansas to hold the warriors in check. Bill joined this force, serving as scout for the commander.

When winter drove the Indians off the warpath,

Bill joined another volunteer group known as the "Red Legged Scouts" who chased bands of white raiders through Missouri and Arkansas. When the scouts were idle, Bill again carried military dispatches to Forts Gibson and Dodge and to other Army posts.

Thus for two years, Bill moved on the fringes of the war, held back from joining the Union Army by his mother's objections. In the summer of 1863, he was on the trail once more, hauling freight to Denver with a small wagon train. He returned to find that his mother's health had broken completely and she died on November 22 of that year.

Except for his sister Julia's marriage to J. A. Goodman a few months before, Bill would have faced the task of looking after his sisters and brother. Julia and her husband moved into the Cody home and Mr. Goodman became the guardian of the younger children.

Three months later, just before his eighteenth birthday, Bill enlisted in the Seventh Kansas Regiment. His Army record describes him as five feet ten inches tall, his complexion fair, his eyes and hair brown. He was a strong, daring, and high-spirited product of the Western plains.

Bill's regiment moved that spring to Tennessee, from where it marched into Mississippi and later northward to Missouri. Bill's skill as a scout was put to use during the skirmishes his regiment fought.

On one of his rides, Bill met Wild Bill Hickok, and the two scouted together until the Southern forces were driven below the Arkansas River.

In the winter of 1864–1865, Bill was sent to the St. Louis Army headquarters on special duty as an orderly. He was very unhappy, for it was hardly the kind of service a plainsman like Bill would choose, and he disliked it heartily. His discouragement was complete when he learned that his brother Charlie had died.

Yet St. Louis was not without its bright side. While there he met a pretty young woman named Louisa Frederici, and they became close friends.

At the end of the war, Bill was sent to Fort Leavenworth to be discharged from the Army. He lost no time in returning to St. Louis to ask Louisa to marry him, and she agreed to, if he would quit the plains after their marriage.

Before that could take place, Bill had to earn some money. First he drove a string of horses from Fort Leavenworth to Fort Kearney, Nebraska. There he met Bill Trotter, a former boss during his pony express days, now an agent for a stagecoach line. Trotter hired Bill to drive a stage between Kearney and Plum Creek for a hundred and fifty dollars a month.

Bill made a dashing figure as he handled the reins over his galloping grays, flicking a rawhide whip so as to strike all four horses in a single motion. He became one of Trotter's best drivers, and the passengers who rocked and bounced inside his gaily painted coach were sure of an exciting ride.

By February, 1866, Bill figured his earnings were enough for his wedding and he hurried to St. Louis to claim his bride. On March 6, a week after his twentieth birthday, he and Louisa were married. She was then twenty-two years old.

As he had promised Louisa, Bill intended to quit his roving life on the plains. The hotel his mother had run until her death stood idle, and he saw in it a chance to go into business. He and his bride, after a honeymoon trip by steamer from St. Louis to Leavenworth, reopened the hotel, calling it the Golden Rule House.

Always mindful of his family, Bill made a home at the hotel for his youngest sisters, Helen and Mary, who were still unmarried. A horde of Bill's friends followed, many of whom forgot to pay for their board and lodging.

A better host than businessman, Bill found after six months that he could not meet his own bills. After he was forced to sell the hotel, Louisa went to Leavenworth to live while her husband tried to find another means of earning a living.

During that time, the Kansas Pacific railroad was being built between Leavenworth and Denver. Until it was finished, freight had to be moved out to the

Smoky Hill district by wagon train. Bill decided to take a hand in this trade and with borrowed money, fitted out a few wagons.

On his first trip, Indians attacked the tiny train. Bill lost everything, barely escaping with his own life. Afoot, he made his way to Junction City, then a wild end-of-the-rails town.

More deeply in debt than ever and discouraged as well, he wandered through the workers' camp, fearful that the best he could find was a dollar-a-day job with the rail crew. Suddenly he was hailed, "Howdy, Bill. What are you doing out here, gawking around like a pilgrim?"

He stared in surprise at Wild Bill Hickok. "Why, hello, Mr. Hickok. I'm—— Well, I'm looking for work. Lost my wagons and freight to some redskins and now I'm——" Bill lacked the heart to go on with his gloomy story.

Wild Bill said, "Better come with me. I'm scouting for the captain over at Fort Ellsworth and he could use another man who knows this country."

"Do you think—— I'd sure like that, Mr. Hickok. Now if I only had a horse——"

"I can fix you up," Wild Bill said. "Come with me. We'll head right for Ellsworth."

With Hickok's help, Bill was hired as an Army scout. Here was the kind of work that suited him perfectly. Galloping across the plains or moving along cautiously to spy upon Indian war parties, he felt alive once more. He wished Louisa could share his enthusiasm for life in the West.

Upon his return to the fort after a scouting trip, he found a letter that filled him with delight. A daughter had been born to him and Louisa on December 16 and had been named Arta. Kept busy around Forts Ellsworth and Fletcher, Bill was unable that winter to pay a single visit to Leavenworth to see the baby.

Now that he had a family, he was in a mood to settle down. His pay as a scout was not enough to make the kind of home he desired for Louisa and Arta. He wanted to make a lot of money quickly.

The new railroad offered what looked to Bill like the chance he sought. He had become friendly with William Rose, a contractor who graded the roadbed ahead of the rail layers. Rose dreamed of building a city on the prairie and invited Bill to join him.

"We'll plot our city, Bill, and give away enough lots to draw people but keep the best for ourselves," Rose said. "After we have the city started, we can find plenty of buyers for our property. We'll make a fortune."

"It sounds good to me, Mr. Rose," Bill said. "Where do you figure to lay out the site?"

"Where the tracks will cross the creek, just a mile from Fort Hays. It's an ideal spot. We'll have it booming in no time."

Setting to work with high hope, Bill helped William Rose lay out the city they called Rome. In thirty days, Rome, Kansas, had two hundred houses, stores and shops, flimsy frame and tarpaper shacks. Bill was so certain of success in this new venture that he sent for Louisa to join him in the home he had built.

Just when the outlook was brightest, the engineers changed their plans. Instead of routing the tracks to Rome, the right-of-way bypassed Rome by three miles. There the town of Hays City was laid out.

In three days, the citizens of Rome moved to the new location. Bill and William Rose were left with their deserted townsite on the prairie.

For the third time since his marriage, Bill Cody was penniless. He had failed as a hotelkeeper, he had been wiped out as a freighter, and now, as a real estate promoter, he was broke again.

Louisa was so discouraged by the repeated setbacks that she took her baby to St. Louis to live with her parents. All that Bill had left was his saddle horse Brigham, a mottled, graceless animal whose shaggy coat gave him the look of a farm drudge.

Having no other choice, Bill hired out as a railroad laborer, pushing a wheelbarrow in the hot sun. His Brigham, until now used only for hunting and scouting, was hitched to a road scraper. As a work horse, he helped his master work on the rail line that had brought him nothing but ill luck.

Chapter 14

BUFFALO HUNTER

Bill Cody flipped over an empty road scraper and set it to scoop up another load of earth. Brigham leaned into his collar and dragged the scraper toward the rising Kansas Pacific roadbed.

A shout from a workman far up the right-of-way was caught up by others. "Buffler . . . buffler headed this way!"

One of the men called, "Bill, why don't you get us some buffler steaks for dinner? You're the best shot in the bunch. Go ahead, Bill, get us some meat."

Bill needed no more urging. Loosening Brigham's traces from the scraper, he threw off the harness and led the horse to a stack of rifles—weapons the crew kept close at hand in case of an Indian attack.

Bill's gun was different from the others. A breech-loading .50 caliber Springfield, it was an Army rifle issued to him when a scout at Fort Ellsworth. It was the truest weapon he had ever handled. He called it his Lucretia Borgia.

Swinging himself upon Brigham, Bill called to the men, "Send out a wagon. I'll have your meat ready before the rig reaches me." Then he started off.

He made a wide circle to approach the buffaloes from down wind to make sure they would not catch his scent. Taking advantage of the animals' poor eyesight, he closed in slowly.

Although he rode bareback, he kept perfect control of his mount. With or without saddle and bridle he could outride any horseman who offered to test his skill.

Without a signal, Brigham began to gather himself for the sprint that would carry his master into shooting position. The horse had a far better sense of timing—the exact moment to begin his charge—than most hunters.

Brigham was upon the buffaloes almost before they were aware of their danger. Running to the right side of a big bull, the horse slowed his pace to that of the animal. Bill swung his rifle to his shoulder and fired downward at the shaggy beast, sending a bullet into its heart.

As the bull rolled to a stop, Brigham dashed ahead and overtook a fat cow. Again Bill's rifle dropped the animal. After the third buffalo had been slain, Bill called out, "That's enough, Brigham. There's plenty of meat here for the boys."

He had the animals skinned and huge roasts and thick steaks carved from the carcasses by the time the wagon reached him. He cut out the tongues and tenderloins and said to the teamster, "Give these to the boss. They're a special treat."

After the wagon had set out for the railroad camp, Bill noticed five Army officers from nearby Fort Hays riding toward him. They smiled among themselves as they eyed Bill's sorry-looking horse and his rough work clothes. The fact that he rode without saddle or bridle also amused them.

"We're doing a little buffalo hunting," one of the officers said. "We want only the tongues and tenderloins; you can have the rest for your rail crew. Come along if you'd care to see how we do it."

"Well, thanks, gentlemen," Bill said. "I'd sure like to see how real hunters work."

With Bill trailing, they loped after eleven buffaloes moving toward a fringe of willows bordering a creek. Bill saw the animals were on their way to water and veered around a knoll to approach them from the side. He was upon them when the Army men were still two hundred yards behind.

A slight pressure from Bill's knee sent Brigham bounding to the flank of the rear buffalo. Bill fired once and the animal dropped. His horse leaped after the next in line. He shot again and another fell dead.

Moving up the file of buffaloes, Bill sent all tumbling to the ground. Only once was his aim off the mark; he used two bullets to bring down one animal. With twelve shots, he had slain eleven buffaloes.

The Army officers, too far behind to get in a single shot, stared in amazement at the unsmiling railroad worker. Bill said gravely, "There're your tongues and tenderloins, gentlemen."

"That . . . that beats anything I ever saw," a captain said. "Never heard of such shooting." He looked closely at Bill. "Say, who are you?"

"Bill Cody."

"Cody? The fellow who scouted for the Army around Ellsworth?"

When Bill nodded, the captain went on, "Well, that explains it. I've heard of your riding and shooting but I never expected to see an exhibition like you just put on."

"I'm sorry if I spoiled your hunt——"

"Forget it, Cody." With a grin, the captain added, "You sort of put us in our place."

In Hays City several days later, Bill met one of the contractors building the Kansas Pacific railroad. The man offered Bill a new kind of job.

"Cody, I've heard that you're a good rifle shot," the contractor said. "How would you like to hunt buffalo to keep my twelve hundred workmen in fresh meat? They need twelve animals a day."

"That would keep a man pretty busy, Mr. Goddard," Bill said, smiling. "Kind of risky, too, with all the redskins prowling around. A fellow hunting alone might be jumped any minute."

"I know it's risky, Cody. But I'll pay a good wage to make it worth while. And you'd have a helper—a butcher to cut up the meat and haul it in by wagon."

"I'm making three dollars a day now—that is, my horse and I together."

"As a hunter, I'll pay you five hundred a month," Mr. Goddard said.

"Five . . . you mean, five hundred . . . Yes, sir! I'll take it, Mr. Goddard. When do you want me to start?"

"Ride over to the camp and go to work," the contractor said.

Happy to be rescued from the drudgery of grading a roadbed, Bill set upon his hunting duties eagerly. With his high wages, he could bring Louisa and the baby to live in Hays City. And he could buy the horse and buggy he had promised his wife. Life began to look better to him.

In that year of 1867, Bill was only one of many hunters who supplied meat to crews stretched along the new rail line. But for every hunter that worked for the railroad, there were a hundred that roamed the plains killing the animals just for their hides.

Although there were millions of buffaloes in the West during the 1860's, the daily slaughter was cutting down the number rapidly. The Indians' hatred for the butchers drove them to kill the whites whenever possible.

To the redmen, the buffalo meant food, shelter, clothing, and weapons. If the herds were wiped out, the tribes would die, too. They fought the buffalo killers to save their own lives. Bill Cody knew well the dangers when he took the job.

He worked out a method of hunting that made him the best of the lot. Coming upon a group of buffalo, he raced to the leaders' sides and forced them to turn to the left. As they ran in a circle, he shot the foremost animals one by one.

When the shoot was over, the dead lay in a small area, making the work of the butcher fairly easy. After the kill, the butcher drove up in a wagon and started his work.

Brigham, the horse Bill bought from a Ute Indian, became his best hunting mount. A wave of Bill's hand, the pressure of a knee, or a spoken word brought instant response. If a buffalo did not fall at Bill's first shot, Brigham would stop to allow a second, but no more. Two misses were all that the horse permitted. After that, he raced on to another target.

As the Indians became more troublesome, soldiers were posted to guard the railroad crews while they worked. They were little protection for Bill, however, since he had to range far out on the prairie to find buffalo.

The herds were always on the move, and at times the hunter spent many hours looking for them. Once he had ridden Brigham twenty miles from camp without sighting a single animal. It was a bad sign; Indian hunting parties had probably driven the buffaloes from the area.

He was not surprised when a band of warriors charged at him from behind a hill. Swinging Brigham around, Bill started the long run to camp.

Glancing back, he counted thirty braves in the pack. Their mounts were fresh while Bill's had had little rest that morning. Here was a test as dangerous as any he had ever faced.

For five miles, Brigham held a safe lead. Then Bill felt the horse begin to tire and the swifter of the Indian ponies drew closer. After another mile, a brave on a spotted mount was eighty yards behind Brigham.

Swinging about, Bill raised his rifle and fired. The Indian's piebald mount crashed to the ground, sending the rider sprawling in the dirt. Soon another pony moved up, and Bill stopped it with a second shot.

Brigham could no longer keep up his swift pace. As he slowed, the Indian pack crept closer and closer. Bullets began to snarl around Bill as the braves tried to bring him down. Bill knew he could not go on much longer.

When within sight of camp, he took hope. The soldiers, hearing the gunfire, were racing out to meet the Indians. The appearance of the troops caused the braves to stop, then turn and flee.

Bill changed to one of the soldiers' fresh horses and joined in the chase. Eight Indians were overtaken and slain in the long running fight that followed.

When Louisa arrived in Hays City, Bill had the promised horse and buggy waiting for her. Whenever he was home, he took her on rides across the plains, hoping she would overcome her fear of the West.

Bill's good intentions had nearly a fatal result. One day as he and Louisa were riding several miles from Hays City, a small party of Indians surprised them and gave chase.

Whipping the horse into a gallop, Bill drove furiously toward town. Armed only with a six-shooter, he knew it was folly to make a fight. Their only hope was to outrun the braves.

With Louisa pale and cringing beside him, Bill urged more speed from the straining horse. The buggy bounced over the rough ground, almost throwing out the riders.

When the braves seemed about to overtake them, Bill held his revolver at Louisa's head, ready to shoot rather than let her fall into the Indians' hands. But the braves broke off the chase when within sight of town, fearing to come closer.

The experience shocked Louisa so much that she returned to St. Louis at once. Several weeks passed before she again ventured out West to rejoin Bill.

Chapter 15

CHAMPION OF THE PLAINS

As the weeks passed, Bill's skill as a hunter made him well known in all the railroad camps along the line. His friends insisted that he was the best on the plains. Before long, he was called on to prove it.

Out at Fort Wallace, in western Kansas, Billy Comstock, the chief of scouts, questioned that claim. Comstock sent word that he wanted to test Bill in a shooting contest—the man who killed most buffalo in a day would be the champion of the plains.

Bill agreed at once. Sure of his ability, he was ready to meet any challenger.

A place twenty miles east of Sheridan, Kansas, was picked for the hunt. As word of the coming match spread, excitement grew and a special train was made up in St. Louis to bring spectators to the sporting event.

Bill's wife, who had again found courage to return to Hays City, was among the more daring women who came out to watch the shoot. Scores of railroad men, soldiers, and plainsmen joined the visitors from St. Louis.

Billy Comstock, a handsome man in his thirties, rode a fine chestnut horse and carried a Henry rifle, a fast-shooting weapon. Bill Cody, only twenty-one, was likewise tall and straight. Louisa looked upon him proudly.

Armed with Lucretia Borgia, his favorite rifle, Bill surprised many spectators when he mounted his shaggy Brigham. They wondered why he had picked the ungainly horse for this match with the well-mounted Comstock. Bill smiled to himself when he observed their doubts.

Before the hunt started, several spotters rode out to find a buffalo herd. After locating one, they divided it and then Bill and his rival set out to start their shoot. Referees trailed the hunters to keep track of the score.

Without a word from Bill, Brigham galloped to the front of the herd and began turning the leaders in a circle. When Bill began to fire, the buffaloes fell within sight of the crowd.

Comstock hunted in a different manner. He picked off his game as he approached from the rear. His kills were stretched in a long line across the prairie.

At the end of the morning's hunt, Bill had chalked up a bag of thirty-eight to Comstock's twenty-three. After a halt for lunch, the shooting was resumed.

When he had killed eighteen more, Bill returned to the crowd and dismounted. Stripping saddle and bridle from Brigham, he said, "I'd like to show you how the Indians hunt."

Clucking to his horse, he rode after another bunch of buffalo, letting Brigham carry him into shooting position without being guided. Twelve more animals fell to Bill's rifle. Then he turned a large bull toward the spectators and chased it straight at them.

Women screamed, men shouted and fell back to escape the shaggy monster. Just when it appeared certain that the bull would plunge into the throng, Bill fired and it fell dead at the edge of the crowd.

Smiling, Bill dismounted and said, "Well, folks, I guess you've seen enough buffalo hunting for one day. I'm going to call a halt if you're satisfied."

One visitor from St. Louis, after catching his breath, remarked, "I never dreamed a man and a horse could do the things I've seen Bill Cody and that Brigham do out here. And I wouldn't believe it if I hadn't seen it."

When Comstock came in, the referees added up the scores. They listed sixty-nine kills for Bill and forty-six for Billy Comstock.

As the crowd cheered the winner, Comstock turned to Bill and shook his hand. "Cody, you're the best—the champion of the plains." With a smile, he added, "I'll fight any man who disputes me."

"Well, thanks, Mr. Comstock," Bill said. "But it

isn't just me. Most of the credit belongs to Brigham. There's no hunting horse like him."

For nearly eighteen months, Bill hunted buffalo to supply the Goddard brothers' railroad crews with meat. During that time, he killed forty-two hundred and eighty animals. For his skill as a hunter, Bill Cody was to become famous, in Europe as well as in America, as Buffalo Bill.

By the time the railroad reached Sheridan in May, 1868, the Indians were in no mood to see more of their buffalo herds slaughtered without trying to stop it. Their bitterness against the whites sent them upon the warpath by the hundreds.

To put down the uprising, the government sent more soldiers into Kansas and made Philip H. Sheridan, the Civil War general, commander of the troops on the plains. As soon as General Sheridan reached his headquarters at Fort Hays, he made plans for a campaign against the tribes.

The Indian war halted work on the railroad and Bill Cody lost his hunting job. Yet he did not have to look long for another. The Army could always use a guide and scout who knew the country, and the quartermaster at Fort Larned was glad to have Bill work for him.

After taking Louisa and his daughter to live in Leavenworth, Bill reported at Fort Larned. He also had to part with his prized horse, Brigham. Since the

Army furnished its scouts with mounts, Bill sold Brigham to a friend, Ike Bonham.

Now twenty-two years old, Bill was about to begin the most adventurous years of his life.

Upon his arrival at Larned, Bill noticed large bands of Kiowa and Comanche Indians in camp nearby. While still claiming to be friendly with the whites, they were restless and made frequent demands on General Hazen, the post commander, for a herd of beef cattle the government had promised them. The cattle were on the way but were slow in arriving.

Chief Satanta, the tribes' leader, was short and stocky and dressed in the uniform of a major general, of which he was proud. He traveled in an Army ambulance drawn by a span of mules, another gift from the commander at Larned, who did all he could to pacify the grasping chief.

Bill knew Satanta well, having met him a few years earlier when most redmen were friendly with the whites. He was disturbed to notice that the Indians were well armed with rifles and ammunition, issued to them by their agent. If the Comanches and Kiowas took a notion to go on the warpath, they were well prepared, Bill saw.

A few days after reaching Fort Larned, Bill was asked by General Hazen to guide him to Fort Harker. The general, riding in a wagon drawn by

six mules, set out with an escort of twenty infantry-
men.

When the party reached Fort Zarah, thirty miles
from Larned, Hazen ordered Bill back to his post.
The only fresh mount available for Bill was a mule,
which he accepted for the return ride.

When halfway home, having reached Pawnee
rock, Bill was surprised by forty braves who raised
their hands in friendly salute and called, "How!" He
recognized them as some of the Indians who had been
around Fort Larned. But now their faces were
smeared with red paint, a sign that they were on the
warpath.

Not wishing to offend the braves, Bill returned
their greeting and held out his hand in a gesture of
friendship. The leader grabbed it tightly and jerked
Bill forward, nearly pulling him off his mount.

Another brave seized the mule's bridle. Others
wrested his rifle and revolver from him and one hit
him on the head with his tomahawk, nearly knocking
him unconscious.

"Come with us," the leader growled.

Bill Cody was a captive of the Comanches.

Chapter 16

ESCAPE FROM THE COMANCHES

Laughing and shouting, Bill's captors led him across the nearby Arkansas River to an Indian village on the far shore. To his surprise, he saw the Comanche chief, Satanta, strut forward to meet the party. Scowling at the prisoner, he said, "Where you been, paleface?"

"I was going after the cattle, the whoa-haws, the white father is sending to your people," said Bill.

"Satanta glad to hear," the chief said, losing his frown. "Where whoa-haws now?"

"My chief, General Hazen, sent me to tell you they are on the way to your village. They're only a few miles away."

"Long swords come with whoa-haws?" Satanta asked.

"Certainly," Bill said. "Many soldiers, many long swords." He now spoke more sharply to the chief.

"Why do your braves strike and abuse me, the scout for the white chief? Why did they take my guns away?"

Satanta shrugged and said, "They wish to see if

you are brave. I tell them give shooting sticks back to long hair."

On orders from their chief, the warriors handed Bill his rifle and revolver. Satanta said, "Now bring whoa-haws to me. I send braves to help."

"I must go alone," Bill said. "The long swords may harm the young men who hit me. We have enough help to drive the whoa-haws."

Satanta nodded and Bill started away at once, riding his mule across the river. From the other side he looked back and saw about a dozen Indians begin to follow. He rode slowly over a ridge but once out of sight, he booted his mount into a gallop and raced toward Fort Larned, fifteen miles away.

By the time the Indians reached the top of the ridge, Bill had a good start. Aware now that they had been tricked, the warriors tore after the scout. The chase continued mile after mile, the Indians' ponies slowly closing the gap between the braves and Bill.

By the time Bill reached a divide between Ash Creek and Pawnee fork, the braves were only a quarter mile behind. Fort Larned was still four miles away. Bill knew that his mule could never cover the distance before being overtaken.

On a high point overlooking Pawnee fork, he glimpsed a wagon and party of soldiers moving out of a thicket beside the stream. Forcing his mount into

Bill saw a party of soldiers appear beside the stream

a final hard sprint, he rushed up to the troops and saw that one of the seven men was a scout called Denver Jim.

"Jim, hide your wagon in the trees," Bill shouted. "There's a pack of redskins after me. Get your boys ready to throw some lead."

The wagon and its escort were barely out of sight before the pursuing Indians swept over the height and tore down upon the thicket. Bill, after slipping from his mule, fell into position beside the soldiers, his rifle ready.

Two Indians, well ahead of the others, raced by but the soldiers held their fire at a signal from Bill. A moment later, the rest of the braves galloped into range of the waiting rifles. Caught in a blast of gunfire, two warriors dropped from their mounts.

Taken by surprise, the remaining Indians whirled away from the ambush. They were so intent upon saving their lives that they failed even to return the fire. When Bill last saw them, they were heading back to their village.

"I guess they've had enough of a chase for today," he said. "Much obliged, boys, for being so handy. I sure needed your help."

"If we knew you were coming, Bill, we'd brought out a bigger reception committee," Denver Jim said with a grin. "As it is, we'd better skip back to the fort before the redskins take a notion to come and see what hit them."

It was almost dark when Bill reached Larned with Denver Jim and the soldiers. He found the post excited by the growing boldness of the Indians. Dick Curtis, the fort's chief of scouts, spoke to Bill of his problems.

"Captain Parker must get word to General Sheridan at Fort Hays about the situation around here," Curtis said. "But none of my scouts wants to tackle the ride at night. It's a dangerous trip, all right, with the country full of redskins. But I have to get that

146

dispatch through to Sheridan." Curtis looked at Bill and left his request unspoken.

"You want me to go, Dick?"

"I was hoping, Bill. I know you've just finished a hard run and I hate to ask——"

"Get me a good horse and I'll get ready, Dick. I've been over the trail more than the other boys."

"Thanks, Bill. You don't know what a help this is to me."

After eating supper and resting for a short time, Bill went to the stables for a horse. Before mounting he took a lariat and tied one end to the bridle and the other to his belt. By 10 o'clock he was on his way to Hays, sixty-five miles away.

As he feared, the heavy darkness caused the horse to step into a hole and fall. Although Bill was thrown to the ground, the rope fastened to his belt prevented his mount from running away.

At Walnut Creek, twenty-five miles from Larned, he rode into a herd of ponies. Too late, he realized that he had blundered upon an Indian village. The wild barking of the camp's dogs awakened the warriors.

Racing across the creek, Bill soon found himself pursued by the aroused braves. By veering into rough country along the stream, then making another turn, he shook off the Indians but in doing so lost his directions.

He risked striking a match to look at his compass. Turning northward toward the Smoky Hill River, he struck the old Santa Fe Trail ten miles from Hays just as daylight was breaking.

Reaching the fort an hour later, he hurried to General Sheridan with his dispatches. It was Bill's first meeting with the famous Civil War soldier, and he liked him at once. Sheridan was likewise impressed with the young scout and the friendship started at this Army outpost was to become a close one in the years ahead.

Noting from the general's startled look that the news was important to him, Bill felt no surprise when Sheridan asked quickly, "Cody, may I ask a very special favor of you—something that the other scouts won't do?"

"I'm ready for anything you ask, sir."

"I have some dispatches that must reach the commander at Fort Dodge without fail. It's a hard ride—ninety-five miles—and the redskins have killed three dispatch carriers between Hays and Dodge in the last few weeks. Knowing that, do you still want to carry my messages?"

"Yes, sir."

"Good. Rest up until four o'clock. Then report to me."

Late that afternoon, Bill was again in the saddle, heading for Dodge. He traveled steadily until daylight, covering seventy miles and reaching Sawlog crossing on Pawnee fork, where a company of soldiers was stationed.

Calling to the pickets so they would not shoot at him by mistake, he entered camp. After eating breakfast and obtaining a fresh mount, he galloped on to Dodge, reaching it at nine o'clock.

"You came through from Hays?" John Austin, the post's chief of scouts, said to Bill in surprise. "How did you manage it, Bill?"

"Shucks, John, I didn't see a redskin on the whole trip."

"It's a miracle, Bill. That's the only word for it."

"Let me get rid of these dispatches and then I want some sleep," Bill said.

When Bill awoke, the post commander called him to his quarters. "Cody, I'm anxious to send some messages to Larned but my scouts—— You seem to be the only one around here who isn't afraid of the Indians. Will you do the job for me?"

"Of course. Larned's my post and I have to get back there anyway. Just give me a fresh horse."

"I'm sorry, Cody, but the best I can offer you is a mule," the commander said.

"All right, I'll ride your mule."

Bill set out in the dark, keeping well off the wagon road between the forts to avoid the Indians. He had no trouble reaching Cook Creek, thirty miles from

Dodge, where he stopped for a drink. As Bill leaned down to dip water with his hat, the mule jerked its halter from his hand and trotted off.

Bill realized that he had forgotten to tie his lariat to the mule's bridle. Unless he could catch the animal, he was in trouble.

He began to run after his mount but it kept fifty yards ahead of him. When he slowed to a walk, the mule walked, too. It headed toward the wagon road and took the turn toward Larned instead of toward Dodge, as Bill thought it would.

Expecting to run into an Indian party at any moment, he continued to chase the mule but could never quite catch up with it. Through the long night he trailed the animal and at daylight reached a hill overlooking Fort Larned. Running and walking, he had covered nearly thirty-five miles afoot.

Footsore, weary, and disgusted with the mule, Bill made one last effort to overtake it. With a swish of its tail, the animal romped out of reach and brayed in triumph.

"You long-eared clown," Bill scolded. "You've played your last trick on me, or anyone else." He lifted his rifle and fired once.

The sound carried to the fort and soon a party of cavalrymen raced out, ready for an Indian fight. Instead, they met Bill trudging toward them with his saddle under an arm.

Bill began to run after his mount

"What's the matter, Bill?" a lieutenant asked. "Lose your horse to the redskins?"

"Redskins or vultures, they can have that hunk of ornery mule hide I left back there. And welcome to it."

Upon reaching the fort, Bill handed his dispatches to Captain Parker and tumbled into bed at Dick Curtis's quarters. While he slept, General Hazen returned to the post.

Curtis aroused the young scout. "The general has some dispatches for Sheridan at Hays, Bill. If you feel up to it, maybe you'll carry——"

Bill yawned and stretched. "Sure, Dick. Only this time, no mule. I ride a horse or I don't go."

Waiting until dark, Bill left Larned for Fort Hays and at daybreak reached General Sheridan's headquarters with Hazen's messages.

"By George, Cody," Sheridan exclaimed, "I can't believe that you've been to Dodge, then to Larned and now back to Hays in such a remarkably short time. Let's see——" The general made some notes on a sheet of paper. "That figures to three hundred and fifty-five miles in about fifty-eight hours. I never heard of such endurance and courage. It's one of the greatest riding feats on record. How did you do it?"

Bill smiled. "I walked some of the way, General—to rest my saddle."

Sheridan looked sharply at Bill. "Cody, a regiment of the Fifth Cavalry will soon be here to campaign against the Indians. I'd like to retain you at Hays and make you chief of scouts for the Fifth. Would you care for that?"

"Why—yes, sir! That would suit me first rate, General."

"Good. Even though you'll be a civilian scout, you will receive a colonel's pay while with this regiment. Now get some sleep, Cody. You've earned a good rest."

Chapter 17

FINDING A LOST ARMY

By the fall of 1868, troops of General Sheridan's command were on the move against the unruly plains Indians. Twelve hundred volunteer cavalrymen were sent to join General George A. Custer's eleven companies of the Seventh Cavalry at Camp Supply in Oklahoma. General W. H. Penrose with three hundred soldiers was down on the Cimarron River searching for Indian camps. One of the scouts with Penrose was Wild Bill Hickok.

On October 3, a column of Fifth Cavalry under General Eugene A. Carr reached Fort Hays where Bill Cody joined it to begin his scouting duties. After a two-day halt to organize its train of seventy-five supply wagons, ambulances, and pack mules, the Fifth Cavalry moved out toward Fort Wallace in western Kansas.

As chief of scouts, Bill was invited to join the officers' mess. Although only twenty-two, he had the respect of older men who knew him to be one of the ablest guides and hunters on the plains. Some of the newer officers looked upon the young scout with open scorn.

This was made plain to Bill when the column made camp on the south fork of the Solomon River. A colonel said to him, "I've been told you're something of a sharp shot, Cody. Do you think you could kill a few buffaloes for our troops?"

"Yes, sir. Send out a couple of wagons to pick up the meat."

The colonel bristled. "I'm not in the habit of ordering out wagons until I'm sure of something to haul."

Bill colored. Without answering, he left camp, quickly shot half a dozen buffaloes and informed the officer the meat was ready. Somewhat doubtfully, the colonel sent out two wagons.

The next day, Bill again went out for buffaloes. He rounded up seven and drove them at a gallop toward camp. When inside the picket lines, he began firing, dropping the animals just before they reached the wagons. He shot the last one in the center of the camp, almost at the colonel's feet.

The camp was in an uproar and the teamsters had a time keeping the horses from stampeding. Angrily the colonel shouted, "What's the meaning of this foolishness, Cody?"

"Why, Colonel, I thought I'd save you the trouble of sending wagons for your meat," Bill said calmly.

"I had the buffaloes furnish their own transportation."

The colonel whirled around and stalked away.

After stopping briefly at Fort Wallace, General Carr took his column westward to Fort Lyon, Colorado, to prepare for a winter campaign against the Indians along the Canadian River. At Lyon he learned that nothing had been heard from General Penrose for three weeks.

Since his only supplies were carried by pack mules, alarm for Penrose's safety gripped the fort. Carr was ordered to move a mule train to his relief. Leaving Fort Lyon in November with a score of wagons, Carr took Bill Cody and four other scouts for guides.

After the column had been out for a few days, a heavy snow covered the trail and forced the wagons to halt. Despite the storm, Bill and his scouts pushed ahead twenty-four miles and found one of Penrose's old camps on a branch of the Cimarron.

Leaving his aides, Bill returned alone to report to General Carr. The next morning the column set out, fighting a blizzard. Taking the lead, Bill rode for eight hours with his left cheek to the storm in order to keep his direction.

When his ear began to pain, he stuffed a piece of saddle blanket into it. Even this did not prevent frostbite; his eardrum was so affected by the cold that as a result he was partly deaf for the rest of his life.

Soldiers and animals suffered alike on that terrible march, but Bill pressed forward until he found Penrose's trail down the west bank of the Cimarron. Acting on his advice that the best wagon route was along a divide on the east side, Carr moved his column southward until it came out on a high tableland that dropped steeply to a valley and creek below.

"Well, Bill, where do we go now?" Carr asked. "We're hung up, high and dry."

"Not at all," said Bill. "We'll take the wagons right down the slope."

"That's impossible, Bill," Carr protested.

"Let me show you," Bill said. He had the wagons moved forward and the wheels chained together to make them skid rather than roll. Then he sent a team of mules over the edge with the first wagon.

Slipping and sliding on stiffened legs, the mules held the supply rig in check until near the bottom of the slope. Then they set out at a gallop to keep the wagon from tumbling upon them, stopping at a level spot that made an ideal camp site.

General Carr was no less amazed than the troopers at the way Bill sent the column, one by one, down the hill.

Bill laughed at their wonder. "There's no telling what an old bullwhacker like me can do with a prairie schooner."

Bill led the column rapidly forward

"I can believe that, Bill," Carr said.

While the troops made camp, Bill scouted the far side of the valley and found where Penrose had been turned back by a blocked trail. In one day, the wagons had covered the same distance it took Penrose's men a week to travel.

Now following a clear trail, Bill led the column

forward rapidly. One day, scouting far ahead of the wagons, he came upon several of Penrose's soldiers trying to get back to Fort Lyon. The men were so weak they could barely walk.

From them, Bill learned their comrades were in camp some distance away. He reported to General Carr, who ordered two companies of troops to move ahead with fifty pack mules loaded with food and warm clothing.

They found Penrose's soldiers in pitiful condition. Out of food for days, the men were almost starved to death. Two hundred of their horses and mules had died from lack of fodder, making it impossible for the troops to go forward or back. The rations Carr brought them saved their lives. Bill was shocked to find his friend, Wild Bill Hickok, as thin and weak as the others.

When the wagons reached the camp, they were unloaded and sent back to Fort Lyon for fresh supplies. Taking charge of all the troops, General Carr waited until they had overcome the effects of their hardship and then picked five hundred to go on with the campaign.

Heading south to the Canadian River, the combined force spent several weeks hunting for Indian villages. Bill spent much of his time shooting antelope, the only game available, to feed the soldiers. When it became clear that the Indians had fled the region,

Carr's army turned back to Fort Lyon, arriving there in March, 1869.

In his report of the campaign, General Carr praised his chief scout highly. He wrote that Bill Cody's ability to find a trail, to guide troops, to judge distances, and to find and shoot game was remarkable. His eyesight was as keen as a man equipped with fieldglasses. He was modest and never quarreled or became excited or noisy. He was at all times a gentleman.

With the campaign over, Bill was given leave to visit his family in St. Louis. His wife was shocked to see him wearing a long mustache, a goatee, and his hair to his shoulders.

"Bill, you must shave and have your hair trimmed," Louisa insisted.

Bill laughed at her surprise. "Why, Louisa, it's the Western style. Mr. Hickok and General Custer look like this. Besides, an Indian fighter must show a real scalplock. If I wear my hair short, it's a sign that I'm a coward."

It took Louisa several days to become used to her husband's appearance. At last she admitted that it added to Bill's good looks and dropped her objections to his shoulder-length hair.

Returning to Fort Lyon, Bill learned that a bunch of horses and mules had been stolen from the post. Taking three scouts, he trailed the two thieves to

Denver and arrested them as they tried to sell the animals.

One escaped on the trip back to Lyon but the other, a desperado named Bill Bevins, was brought in and locked up. He later broke from the guardhouse and sent back word that he would kill Bill Cody on sight. Before that happened, he was caught robbing a stagecoach and jailed in Wyoming.

Spring sent the Indians back on the warpath, and General Sheridan ordered Carr and his Fifth Cavalry to Fort McPherson, Nebraska, to punish them. Bill again led the civilian scouts.

Finding fresh signs on the north fork of Beaver Creek, Bill took his scouts and a squad of troopers ahead to spy on the tribes. Carr's cavalry went into camp to await the scouts' report.

Reaching a hill twelve miles to the north, Bill's group saw a large Sioux village three miles away. Thousands of ponies grazed around some four hundred lodges.

Bill whistled softly and turned to Lieutenant Ward, the squad leader. "Now there's a real prize for you, Lieutenant. Twenty-five hundred or three thousand redskins in that pack. We'd better tell the general pronto."

Ward ordered a corporal to the rear with the message. The trooper had gone only a short way before a hunting party of braves turned him back.

Bill took his scouts ahead to spy on the tribes

"Lieutenant, let me take that message to Carr," Bill said. Setting out at a lope, he came upon the same band of hunters and fired upon them at long range. Surprised, and evidently thinking that a large force of whites was about to attack, the braves drew aside.

They hesitated just long enough for Bill to get between them and Carr's camp. When they saw that the scout was alone, they took up the chase but were outrun and Bill carried his message to Carr. The general ordered his men to advance at once.

When the troops approached the Indian village, they found five hundred mounted warriors drawn up in a line to protect the camp. Behind them, squaws and children worked feverishly to pack their belongings and flee.

General Carr's orders went out to his officers, "Break through the center of the Indian line and destroy their village."

Before the main assault could begin, however, a lieutenant and his company charged a group of warriors at the left. The soldiers were soon surrounded and Carr was forced to send much of his cavalry to their rescue. By the time the company was saved, the general's plan of attack was ruined, and he had to withdraw to protect his supply train.

The next morning the troops moved forward once more but found no Indians, only the abandoned gear and debris of the village. Following its trail, the cavalrymen surprised three hundred warriors in a ravine. After the fight that resulted, the Indians broke into small bands and escaped, leaving many ponies in the soldiers' hands.

During the fight, Bill Cody had a close call. While crossing a creek, an Indian surprised him and fired, killing his horse. Bill was thrown to the ground just as another warrior joined in the attack.

The scout turned his rifle upon the brave, but the shot missed. Caught in a dangerous spot, Bill scrambled for cover and was pinned down until an advance guard of troopers came to his rescue.

In spite of his narrow escape, Bill came out of the

battle with a warrior's horse which was to become famous as Powder Face. A large-sized pony of Indian breed, he was buckskin in color and had a dark mane and tail. Swift and strong, Powder Face had great endurance, the kind of mount Bill needed for his hard riding.

Because of their long march from Fort Lyon, General Carr's force was now short of rations. Bill rode sixty miles to Fort Kearney, the nearest Army post, for the needed supplies.

When the Fifth Cavalry reached Fort McPherson, situated near where North Platte, Nebraska, now stands, three companies of Pawnee Indians joined Bill's force of scouts. Led by Major Frank North, the tribesmen were eager for battle against their age-old enemies, the Sioux.

Bill had never seen troops quite like the Pawnees. They had been issued regular cavalry uniforms but had their own ideas about how to wear them. A number of the braves wore overcoats, and others had discarded the pants for breechclouts. A few wore black hats but no shirts.

For all their oddity of dress, they were well drilled, took pride in their position with the Army, and obeyed no one but their white leader, Major North. As horsemen and crack shots, they were about the best on the plains.

At McPherson, General Carr summoned Cody and

said, "Bill, I'm making you the chief of scouts of the Department of the Platte. That will bring the Pawnees under your command."

"That's very good of you, sir," Bill said. "But Major North's the only man who can handle that pack of Pawnees."

"That's all right, Bill," Carr said. "I'm sure North will work closely with you. By the way, you could use a little extra pay, couldn't you?"

Bill smiled. "I wouldn't turn it down."

"You're worth more to me than what you're getting paid for," the general said. "We're going to have a busy summer and I'm depending heavily on you."

Chapter 18

BILL CODY BECOMES BUFFALO BILL

General Carr's cavalry pushed toward the Republican River without overtaking the Sioux. Reaching the mouth of Beaver Creek, the troops made camp for the night. The teamsters unhooked their mules from the wagons and turned them out to graze.

Before the cooks could start supper, one of the herders, an arrow sticking in his back, dashed into camp shouting, "The Sioux! The redskins are running off the mules."

Without stopping to resaddle, Bill Cody leaped upon his horse. Frank North and the Pawnees were mounted just as quickly. Together they raced out to the attack.

They came upon fifty Sioux warriors shouting and waving blankets to stampede the mules. Surprised to find the feared Pawnees with the cavalry, the Sioux forgot about the livestock and ran for their lives.

Riding his fleet horse, Bill held the lead until a Pawnee chief on a shabby-looking buckskin pony shot past him with amazing speed. Thereafter he paid more attention to the buckskin than he did to the fleeing Sioux.

The chase, in which several of the enemy were killed, continued for fifteen miles. When the scouts turned back Bill rode over to Major North and said, "Frank, one of your chiefs is riding a big pony that's about the fastest critter on four legs I've ever seen. Is there any chance for me to get him into my string?"

"It's a government horse, Bill," North said. "Talk to the chief and try to make a swap. It's all right with me."

The Indian was unwilling at first to trade horses, but several gifts that Bill offered in addition changed his mind. Bill called his new mount Buckskin Joe, and while he scouted with the Fifth Cavalry he rarely went into battle except on the famous war horse.

The slippery Sioux continued to elude Carr's force. The Pawnees were not annoyed—one sport was as good as another. If they could not hunt Sioux, they could always hunt buffalo.

Coming upon a small herd, twenty Pawnees surrounded the animals and managed to kill thirty-two. Bill then spoke up and offered to show his method of hunting. Curious to see whether "long hair" could equal their skill, the Pawnees held back when the next herd came into sight.

Mounted on Buckskin Joe, Bill killed thirty-six buffaloes in a half-mile run. It was a feat the Indians could appreciate, and their respect for him soared.

Carr's cavalry pressed on day after day eager for a clash with the Sioux. Late one afternoon as Bill and Major North rode ahead of the column to pick a camp site, they ran into a large band of the enemy. The Sioux leaped to the chase at once. Before the scouts could get out of rifle range, Bill had his quirt shot out of his hand and a bullet hole in his hat.

From a high point within sight of the Pawnee scouts, North rode his horse in a circle. It was a signal that hostiles were near. The Pawnees raced out and drove off the Sioux.

The Indian trail led the Fifth Cavalry to the sand hills of northeastern Colorado. At Summit Springs, the scouts discovered eighty-four Sioux lodges. Leaving the Pawnees to keep watch, Bill rode back to inform Carr. The general at once sent out a strong force to engage the enemy.

Leading the troops in a circle to approach the village from the north, Bill rode with the cavalry in its surprise attack. Charging through the camp, the soldiers routed the Indians, who broke up into small bands as they fled.

In the camp, the troopers found two white women, captives of the Sioux. One had been slain to prevent her rescue, the other was seriously wounded. Major

Frank North killed Tall Bull, a noted chief, in this fight.

Guiding a company of cavalry, Bill took up the trail of a hundred Sioux fleeing into the northwest. The chase continued for two days, but then it was discovered that another force of Sioux had joined the first. On the third day, the troopers ran into six hundred warriors.

Closing ranks, the braves charged the troopers and drove them into a ravine. After a fight at long range, the Indians withdrew.

It took several days for Carr's scattered companies to regroup. They were soon engaged in another battle with three hundred warriors. This time the soldiers routed the braves and seized a large number of their ponies.

In this fight, Bill Cody captured a swift horse which he later trained as a racing pony. He called the mount Tall Bull.

With the Indians now well scattered, Carr moved his cavalry to Fort Sedgwick. They had hardly reached the post before reports of fresh Indian outbreaks were received. The most daring was the derailing of a Union Pacific freight train near O'Fallon's station. Two companies of cavalry under Major Brown were ordered from Fort McPherson to punish the raiders.

Ordered to scout for Major Brown, Bill Cody and

Frank North left at once for McPherson. There, in the autumn of 1869, Bill met a man who was to have a great influence upon his life.

This man was Colonel E. Z. C. Judson, who wrote blood-chilling "dime novels" under the name of Ned Buntline. He came West in search of a new hero about whom he could write thrilling tales of Indian warfare and life on the plains.

Accounts of Frank North's adventures as an Indian fighter had appeared in Eastern newspapers. Buntline tried at first to cast North in the role of hero, but the scout was not interested. He suggested that the man for him was Bill Cody.

Good-natured and obliging, Bill was willing to grant any favor asked of him. "Sure, I can spin some yarns," he told Buntline, "but they're no different from what the other boys can give you. We all did about the same thing."

"Let me be the judge of that," Buntline said. "You just answer my questions."

When Bill rode as scout with Major Brown's expedition from Fort McPherson, Ned Buntline went along, mounted on Powder Face. In the days he spent with Bill, Buntline became excited over his discovery. The handsome young scout was the perfect character for his novels.

Major Brown's campaign amounted to little. From O'Fallon's station his troops followed the Indian trail

169

along the North Platte River. But the raiders had a safe lead and were never overtaken. The soldiers returned to McPherson, and Ned Buntline went back East to write.

Within a few weeks his first Western story, "Buffalo Bill, the King of the Border Men," was published and read widely. The twenty-three-year-old scout was on his way to fame.

No longer was he to be plain Bill Cody. Buntline had created and turned the spotlight on Buffalo Bill, a new symbol of the American West.

Dozens of Buntline's novels about Buffalo Bill appeared in the next few years. There was little truth or reality in them. Fiction was piled so thickly upon fact that the real part Bill Cody played in subduing the West was all but lost. That did not bother Ned Buntline. He was interested only in writing wild and robust stories for his thousands of readers.

By October, 1869, the various Army commands were in winter quarters at their western posts. His scouting duties ended for the year, Bill remained in Fort McPherson without a job.

The idle troops found sport in horse racing, and Bill was quick to meet their challenge. Riding Tall Bull against the cavalry's best, he won enough money to keep him in funds until another job turned up.

That winter two parties of wealthy Englishmen arrived at McPherson to hunt on the plains. Bill offered to guide them and run their camps. His work pleased them so much that they spread word about the remarkable Buffalo Bill in their homeland.

Before the visitors left, a special horse race was arranged to entertain them. Bill agreed to ride Tall Bull against a cavalryman mounted on the regiment's fastest horse.

This was not to be an ordinary contest, however. In the course of the mile run, Bill promised to leap on and off Tall Bull eight times while galloping at full speed.

Riding bareback, he seized the horse's mane with his left hand and rested his right on the withers. Thus he leaped to the ground and sprang back, winning the race despite the handicap. It was a circus trick he had practiced with Tall Bull for hours.

Between races and his hunting, Bill had time to work on a cabin outside the fort stockade. He wanted it ready for his family who were coming west in the spring.

Not only Louisa and Arta joined him early in 1870 but his two youngest sisters, Helen and Mary, came out from Leavenworth to share his home. Three women and a young daughter now depended upon him for support.

Soon after Bill began his scouting duties that year, a band of Sioux ran off a government contractor's horse herd and some cavalry mounts, including Powder Face. Leading a large body of troops, Bill followed the Indian trail for sixty miles. Darkness forced the soldiers to camp, but Bill moved ahead and found the raiders four miles off.

Early the next morning, the troops closed in for a surprise attack. They struck just as the Sioux were mounting. In the hot chase that followed, one warrior had his horse shot from under him. He leaped upon another pony already burdened with one rider.

Taking after the two, Bill Cody gained rapidly and when within thirty feet of them opened fire. His bullet passed through both riders and they fell dead.

Seeing a warrior escaping on Powder Face, Bill raced after him, but the war pony was too swift. The powerful animal carried his Indian rider to safety, and Bill never saw his horse again.

The troopers regained thirty-two stolen horses and returned to Fort McPherson, covering one hundred and thirty miles in two days.

On November 26, 1870, Buffalo Bill became a father for the second time. Proud of his little son, he named him Kit Carson Cody after the famous scout and plainsman he had met at Fort Laramie.

But Bill's growing family added to his worries. He had little money and he faced another winter without a job. No one cared to challenge Tall Bull to more races and no hunting parties appeared on the plains.

Sure of himself in any work that had to do with

horses, he thought seriously of moving to an Eastern city to become a fire engine driver, or even a coachman.

Before this became necessary, an odd job—odd for Buffalo Bill at any rate—turned up. Because of an outbreak of petty crimes around McPherson, there was need of a justice of the peace to punish the offenders. Buffalo Bill was given the job even though he "knew no more about law than a mule does about singing," as he admitted.

One of his first duties was the reading of a marriage ceremony. He couldn't find the right words in a law book. More frightened than the bridegroom, Bill had the couple join hands and declared them man and wife, adding, "who God and Buffalo Bill have joined together, let no man put asunder."

At another time, the victim of a horse theft came to Bill for a writ of replevin to recover the animal. Not knowing what the law term meant, Bill took his rifle Lucretia, mounted his horse and called on the suspected thief. He came back with the pony, remarking as he patted his rifle, "That's the best writ of replevin ever invented."

Buntline's stories about Buffalo Bill were stirring a wide curiosity about the young scout and hunter. The plains, for the time being, were almost free of Indian trouble, and well-known people from the East were joining in the buffalo slaughter. Many of them made it a point to see in the flesh the hero of Buntline's novels.

General Sheridan in September, 1871, invited a group of leading New York and Chicago residents on a spectacular hunting expedition. He detailed one hundred cavalrymen to escort the visitors and loaded sixteen wagons with baggage and supplies. Everything was on a grand scale.

The general hired Buffalo Bill as scout and guide for the party. The job was to add greatly to his reputation.

Chapter 19

THE GREAT SHOWMAN

General Sheridan's hunting guests, among whom was James Gordon Bennett, a New York newspaper editor, gazed in amazement at a handsome figure who greeted them at Fort McPherson. His wiry frame was clad in a new suit of buff-colored buckskin fringed in the best Western style. A white sombrero was atop his shoulder-length hair.

Mounted on a white horse, Buffalo Bill made a magnificent picture, more dashing and romantic even than Ned Buntline had described. His dark piercing eyes were never forgotten by anyone who had looked into them. In the sport that followed, he proved to the visitors that his fame as a horseman, crack shot, guide, and hunter was based on solid accomplishment.

When he returned to New York, Editor Bennett glorified Buffalo Bill in his accounts of the hunt. Called the "beau ideal of the plains," Bill became the best-known Westerner of the time.

That fall, the Fifth Cavalry was sent from Mc-Pherson to Arizona. As the regiment's chief of scouts,

Buffalo Bill was expected to go along. Just before the troops entrained, General Sheridan wired the commander, "Don't take Cody." That order was another turning point in Bill's life. Had he gone south to the desert, he might have missed the opportunities opening to him.

Sheridan wanted Buffalo Bill to remain behind to guide another hunting party, this time a group of millionaires, General Custer, and the Grand Duke Alexis of Russia. For special entertainment, Sheridan asked Bill to induce Chief Spotted Tail and a hundred Sioux warriors to put on war dances, a sham battle, and Indian buffalo hunts.

Although the Sioux were still hostile to Bill, whom they called "Pa-has-ka," the long-haired chief, the scout disguised himself as a warrior and entered the Indian village.

Honored by the request, Spotted Tail brought a band of his braves to the white men's hunting camp and put on a show that thrilled and delighted the Russian duke. Among the braves was Two Lance, who shot an arrow entirely through a buffalo running at top speed. He was reputed to be the only Indian able to do this.

Urged by Sheridan to accept the invitation of Bennett and others to visit the East, Bill finally agreed. Glad of her husband's social success, Louisa also encouraged him. Perhaps it would be a means of taking the Cody family away from the West she still feared and disliked so heartily.

Bill reached the East at a time when Ned Buntline's play dramatizing Buffalo Bill's career was appearing in a New York theater. The crowd gave Bill an ovation when he appeared one night, and the manager offered him five hundred dollars a week if he would take the chief role in the play.

It was a tempting offer for a twenty-six-year-old plainsman, but he decided a government mule could act better than he could and he refused it. Besides, the crowds and the big city were more frightening than Indians and other Western dangers.

Bill returned to Fort McPherson just at the time that an Indian war party raided the post horse herd. Quickly shedding his city clothes, he led a company of the Third Cavalry, which had replaced the Fifth, after the stolen stock. Among his six scouts was J. B. Omohundro, known as Texas Jack.

For two days the troops followed the Indian trail. Riding well ahead of the cavalry, Bill and his aides reached the Platte River and found a camp of thirteen braves watching over the stolen animals.

Fearing discovery if the scouts returned to the main force, Bill decided to attack at once. Astride Buckskin Joe, he charged forward. Two warriors fired at him, and one bullet creased his scalp, gouging a five-inch wound. Wiping the blood from his eyes, Bill killed the brave who had shot him, then fell back to wrap a handkerchief around his head. The wound was the only one he suffered in his many Indian fights.

The sound of gunfire brought up the cavalrymen at a gallop. Six of the thirteen Indians were slain, and most of the horses recovered. For his part in this action, Buffalo Bill was voted the Congressional Medal of Honor, which was taken from him many years later because, as a civilian, he could not hold a military award.

Scouting duties kept Bill busy until August, 1872, when the birth of Orra, his second daughter, called him home. There a letter from Buntline awaited, urging him to come East and appear in a new play he planned. Frightened by the prospect, Bill couldn't bring himself to accept. He continued to scout and guide hunters until fall.

Honors now came to Bill. The Nebraska governor made him a colonel in the national guard. Without consulting him, his friends elected him to the Nebraska legislature. Bill refused to serve, saying that politics was too deep for him.

Buntline kept after Bill to appear in a play made up entirely of frontier scenes. At last, taking Wild Bill Hickok and Texas Jack with him, Buffalo Bill went to Chicago to meet the writer.

The play that resulted was first staged on December 16. Bill and his companions suffered from stage fright and forgot their parts but by telling stories of the West they satisfied the audience. Before the eyes of people who read about Buffalo Bill in Buntline's dime novels, the man became a live hero. That was enough to make him welcome on any stage in the country.

In the next four years, he spent his winters as Buffalo Bill the stage hero and his summers as Buffalo Bill the Western hunter. He had moved his family to Rochester, New York, where Louisa and the children lived well on his earnings, which were now fairly large.

In April, 1876, the death of his six-year-old son Kit Carson crushed Buffalo Bill. The tragedy took place just as the Sioux Indians were making their last desperate effort to drive the whites from the Dakota Black Hills.

Seeking any action that would take his mind off the loss, Bill started West to serve the Army once more as a scout. Soon after he rejoined the Fifth Cavalry, the nation was shocked by General Custer's disaster on the Little Big Horn.

Wearing his stage costume—a Mexican suit of black velvet, splashed with scarlet and trimmed with silver buttons and lace—Buffalo Bill took part in the battle of War Bonnet Creek in the Black Hills district. At one stage in the fight, Bill and fifteen scouts

Bill snatched the war bonnet and held it aloft in victory

rode out to rescue two dispatch carriers being chased by a score of Sioux. Suddenly the warriors turned to skirmish with the whites.

One of the Indians, a proud young chief named Yellow Hand, called out to Bill in the Sioux tongue, "I know you, Pa-has-ka. If you want to fight, come and fight me." The chief rode back and forth in front of the men, defying Bill.

Answering the challenge, Bill galloped straight at the Indian, who likewise raced forward. When the two were thirty yards apart, Bill fired and killed Yellow Hand's horse. Just as the chief fell to the ground, Bill's mount stepped into a hole and Bill went down.

Springing to their feet, the two were only twenty paces apart when they raised guns at the same moment. Both fired. The Indian missed. Leaping forward, Bill snatched the war bonnet from the slain chief and held it aloft in victory.

While the duel was being fought, neither red nor white soldiers made a move to interfere. But when they saw their leader fall, the Indians raced toward Bill howling for his scalp. The cavalrymen surrounded him and fought off the charge.

During the Black Hills war, Buffalo Bill added to his fame as a scout and messenger. Riding in rain and darkness, through broken plains swarming with Sioux on the warpath, he risked his life daily to carry dispatches between the commanders in the field.

When he could be spared, he returned East and continued his stage career. With his profits, he bought a large cattle ranch near North Platte in partnership with his fellow scout, Frank North. On the outskirts of the city itself, he built Welcome Wigwam, a fine home for his family.

The years between 1877 and 1882 were marked by Buffalo Bill's growing success as a showman. He appeared in crowded theaters in all parts of the nation. Looking ahead to the days when he could retire amid the plains and mountains he loved, he took over a four-hundred-thousand-acre tract in the Big Horn basin of Wyoming. He dreamed of making his TE ranch a showplace where he could entertain his friends without thought of cost.

But first another dream became a breath-taking reality. His stage plays were limited to noisy, unreal dramas of life on the plains. He wanted to show the real thing—Indians, cowboys, rough riders, sharpshooters, the pony express, buffaloes, and a stagecoach holdup. For this he would need an outdoor arena with room for action.

Buffalo Bill's "Wild West, Rocky Mountain and Prairie Exhibition" opened in Omaha, Nebraska, on May 17, 1883. It was unlike anything ever offered to entertain the public.

Bill himself, then thirty-seven years old, was a striking figure as he rode into the arena. His long hair, wide mustache, goatee, and blazing eyes held the attention of thousands of spectators.

The show began with a bareback pony race between Indians and was climaxed by a frightening battle between whites and redmen. In between, cowboys rode bucking broncos and roped Texas steers, pony express riders raced around the lot, and the Deadwood stage was held up by masked road agents. Rifle experts broke glass balls and clay pigeons.

It was the true West brought within sight, hearing, and smell of the fascinated crowd. The rattle of wheels, the thunder of hoofs, the clank of spurs, the crack of firearms, the odor of cattle and gunpowder —all were there in abundance.

The Wild West show was an instant hit, and Buffalo Bill embarked upon his most profitable years. In 1885 a million persons saw the show, and he made a hundred thousand dollars.

In 1886 he took his hundreds of performers and animals to London where royalty of all Europe, as well as great crowds of Britons, were awed by the daring Wild West feats. Buffalo Bill was now as well known in Europe as he was in America.

After touring the United States for two more years, he took the show across the Atlantic again and repeated his triumphs in France, Italy, and other countries.

The exhibition reached its peak in 1893 when it

183

appeared opposite the Columbian Exposition at Chicago. In that year, six million persons enjoyed the spectacle and Buffalo Bill cleared a million dollars.

Some of the performers with Buffalo Bill became famous in their own right. Annie Oakley, Lillian Smith, Johnny Baker, and Seth Clover delighted crowds with their shooting skill, but the loudest cheers always went up when Buffalo Bill performed. He was a practical marksman who was equally expert with a rifle, a Colt revolver, a Derringer, a shotgun, or a carbine.

Besides his many services as a builder of the West, Buffalo Bill pioneered in four enterprises that became flourishing industries.

With Ned Buntline, he created the Western story, a form of literature now more popular than ever.

His Wyoming estate became the first dude ranch where dozens of guests were entertained for weeks by the generous host. From this idea has grown the prosperous dude ranch industry that dots the entire West.

Wild West shows were an outgrowth of Buffalo Bill's own experience on the Western frontier and earned millions of dollars for him. Other showmen and circuses copied his methods, to their personal gain.

Buffalo Bill was the first to see the possibility of recording on motion picture films the epics of Western life. The W. F. Cody Historical Pictures Company reproduced in 1914 the battle between Indians and American soldiers at Wounded Knee Creek, a picture that was the forerunner of the present "horse operas," or Western movies.

By his own efforts, Buffalo Bill put his name on the map of the United States. The town of Cody, Wyoming, was planned by him, and its first buildings were erected at his expense. Cody stands at the eastern gateway to the Yellowstone National Park, and a striking statue of the scout in action marks one end of its main street.

Buffalo Bill made his last public appearance at Portsmouth, Virginia, in 1916. He died January 10, 1917, at the age of 71 in Denver, Colorado. He rests now in his beloved West, which he helped so much to develop, in a tomb blasted from solid rock on Lookout Mountain, twenty miles from Denver.

The renown enjoyed by Buffalo Bill is well illustrated by an incident that took place in Minneapolis, Minnesota, when the great showman once appeared at the W. D. Gordon Company store to buy some furniture for his sister. Cody was traveling with his Wild West show and as usual wore his fringed buckskin suit.

After taking the order, Mr. Gordon asked, "Where shall I send the bill, Mr. Cody?"

"Oh, send it to Buffalo Bill, America."

REAL DATES IN THE LIFE OF
BUFFALO BILL

1846 February 26, born near Le Claire, Iowa. (This date entered in family Bible in Bill's own hand. The year on his tombstone is 1845.)

1853 Cody family moves to Kansas.

1857 May, at age of eleven, gets job with Russell, Majors & Waddell as "extra" with wagon train.

1857–58 Spends winter at Fort Bridger with four hundred stranded bullwhackers.

1859 Joins gold rush to Colorado.

1859–60 Traps furs with David Harrington.

1860–61 Rides for pony express.

1862 Joins "Red Legged Scouts" in Kansas-Missouri border war.

1864 Enlists in Seventh Kansas Regiment for Civil War duty.

1865 Meets Louisa Frederici in St. Louis.

1866 Becomes stagecoach driver; March 6, marries Louisa Frederici at St. Louis; December 16, daughter Arta born; Bill scouts for Army at Fort Ellsworth.

1867–68 Hunts buffalo for railroad building crews.

1868 Becomes chief of scouts for Fifth Cavalry under General Sheridan.

1869 Meets Ned Buntline, who popularizes name Buffalo Bill.

1870 November 26, Kit Carson Cody born.

1871 Guides General Sheridan's hunting party of prominent Eastern guests.

1872 Guides Grand Duke Alexis of Russia on Western hunt; August, daughter Orra born; Bill elected to Nebraska legislature but refuses to serve; December 16, makes first appearance on stage in Buntline drama of West.

1876 April, Kit Carson Cody dies; Bill scouts for Army in Sioux war, fights duel with Chief Yellow Hand.

1877–82 Tours United States as actor.

1883 February 9, daughter Irma born; May 17, opens his Wild West show at Omaha, Nebraska.

1886 Wild West show makes first appearance in Europe.

1893 Wild West show at peak, plays to six million spectators at Chicago Columbian Exposition.

1914 Makes Western movie.

1916 November 11, makes final public appearance at Portsmouth, Virginia.

1917 January 10, dies at Denver, Colorado, at age of 71

MORE BOOKS TO READ ABOUT
BUFFALO BILL AND THE WEST

There are many good books about Buffalo Bill and the West. Some are:

THE PONY EXPRESS, by Samuel Hopkins Adams, published by Random House

FAMOUS SCOUTS, by Charles H. L. Johnston, published by L. C. Page & Company

LITTLE ANNIE OAKLEY, by Stewart H. Holbrook, published by The Macmillan Company

ADVENTURES OF BUFFALO BILL, by Colonel William F. Cody, published by Harper & Brothers

BUFFALO BILL, by Shannon Garst, published by Julian Messner, Inc.

WESTERN HORSEMAN, a publication

Other *REAL* books about the West are:

THE REAL BOOK ABOUT COWBOYS, by Michael Gorham

THE REAL BOOK ABOUT THE WILD WEST, by Adolph Regli

THE REAL BOOK ABOUT THE TEXAS RANGERS, by Allyn Allen

REAL books with something in them about the earlier West are:

THE REAL BOOK ABOUT ANDREW JACKSON, by Harold Coy

THE REAL BOOK ABOUT GEORGE WASHINGTON, by Harold Coy

THE REAL BOOK ABOUT DANIEL BOONE, by William Cunningham

INDEX

Le Claire, Iowa, 13
Long, George, 122

McCarthy brothers, Indian attack, 62–69
  wagon train, 59
Majors, Alec, 57–60
Mochila, 102–103

North, Major Frank, 163–169, 182

Oakley, Annie, 184
Omohundro, J. B. (Texas Jack), 177–178

Pah-Ute Indian war, 104
Pawnees, as Army scouts, 163–167
Penrose, General W. H., 153, 158
Plum Creek Indian raid, 62–69
Pony express, *see* Express, pony
Powder Face (horse), 163

Rose, William, 127–128
Russell, Majors, & Waddell, supply company, 57

Satanta, Chief, 141, 143–144
Sheridan, General Philip H., 140, 148, 152, 153, 160, 174–175
Simpson, Lew, 73, 80
  Indian attack, 80–88
  wagon train destroyed, 77–78
Slade, Alf, 103, 105, 113, 116, 120
Slavery issue in Kansas, 24, 44–45, 48, 55
  Cody a Jayhawker, 121
Smith, Joe, and men, destroy wagon train, 77–78
Spotted Tail, Chief, 176

Tall Bull (horse), 168
  race, 171
Texas Jack, 177–178
Trotter, Bill, 101–102, 124
Turk, Bill's dog, 1–19
  rescue of, 16

Weston, Missouri, 14, 20
Woods, George, 77

Yellow Hand, Chief, 181